STADIUM

 Alan Patching is the Chief Executive Officer of MTM Stadium Management Limited, the entity which manages Stadium Australia Trust. He acts as the owner's representative and is Project Director for the development of the Stadium.

Alan's interest in photography is a legacy from the days that he worked part time as a freelance photo-journalist while studying for his quantity surveying qualifications at what was then the Queensland Institute of Technology. He has had numerous photographs and articles published both in Australia and overseas.

Recognised as one of Australia's leading international business presenters, he is also the author of several business related books and audio albums. This is his first photographic anthology.

Alan Patching is represented by Saxton Speakers Bureau of Melbourne.

STADIUM

The project director's diary Alan Patching

Allen & Unwin

The schedule of subcontractors included is that advised by Multiplex to the owners in regular monthly reports.

The schedule of names included is from Multiplex site office records of people who worked on the site.

Every reasonable effort has been made in compiling and checking the information used in preparing this publication to ensure that it is accurate. The publishers and/or Alan Patching shall not be responsible for continued currency of information or for negligence, errors or other discrepancies or for any consequence arising therefrom.

First published in 1999 by
Allen & Unwin
9 Atchison Street, St Leonards NSW 1590 Australia
Phone: (61 2) 8425 0100
Fax: (61 2) 9906 2218
E-mail: frontdesk@allen-unwin.com.au
Web: http://www.allen-unwin.com.au

National Library of Australia
Cataloguing-in-Publication entry:

　Patching, Alan.
　　Stadium : the project director's diary.

　ISBN 1 86508 173 6.

　1. Stadium Australia (Homebush Bay, N.S.W.). 2. Olympic Games
　(27th : 2000 : Sydney, N.S.W.) - Buildings, structures, etc.
　3. Stadiums - New South Wales - Homebush Bay - History.
　4. Stadiums - New South Wales - Pictorial works. I. Title.

725.82709944

Set in 10 pt Berkeley Book
Printed and bound by South China Printing, Hong Kong / China
Cover and internal design: Steven Dunbar

Acknowledgements

With thanks to:

the people at all levels of all the organisations who worked together to deliver the Stadium.

Colin Balchin, George Spooner, Grace Testa and Samantha Hawken-Lau from The Lab.

Stephen Rix, Chairman of MTM Stadium Management Limited.

Maria Humphreys and Nicole Uren.

Patrick Gallagher, Annette Barlow and Steven Dunbar.

Bob Peters, a genius behind a camera, who always willingly provided advice to make my
pictures that little bit better.

And a special thanks to Multiplex for contributing to the photographic equipment with which this essay was
recorded.

In memory of John Schooling, an architect who passed away unexpectedly in early September 1999. John
worked full-time on the Stadium project, managing the quality control of the architectural documentation. He
contributed with experience, skill and enthusiasm and always with the highest professionalism. All involved
with the delivery of Stadium Australia will remember him with love and respect. He will be sadly missed.

This book is dedicated to the athletes whose performance at Stadium Australia will be a source of inspiration for many, to those they inspire and, above all, to my main source of inspiration, my family.

Official Fundraising Project

All author's royalties from the sale of this book will be

donated to the Sydney 2000 Paralympic Games.

Contents

Foreword

RALPH DOUBELL

Olympic Gold Medallist, 1968

Director of Stadium Australia Management

Director of Relationship Management at Deutsche Bank

It was 15 October 1968. The Azteca Stadium in Mexico City was packed with 70 000 people. My race, the 800 metres, was the last event of the day, starting at 5 p.m. It was hot and sultry. Rain had fallen earlier in the afternoon and the track was still wet. The Starter called 'On your marks' and eight nervous athletes lined up to race for the Gold Medal. All of a sudden the athlete in the lane next to me broke. As we were recalled to the starting line I was told that if I broke again I would be disqualified. What was going on? The Starter had made a mistake. I had not made the break. What should I do? Dispute the call and lose my concentration? Or just ignore the mistake? I ignored the mistake.

When the gun finally went I started slowly, very slowly and even now 31 years later I can still recall almost every stride of that race.

With 300 metres to go I moved into second place behind Wilson Kiprugut from Kenya. I was tempted to make a break for it, but it was far too early. I had to stick to my race plan.

My coach Franz Stampfl and I had discussed it many times. Wait until the top of the bend and then kick. I kicked with 150 metres to go. Kiprugut was still in front but I had made up two metres. I drew level with him and kept yelling to myself, 'you can do it, you can do it, kick harder'. With 50 metres to go I broke contact with Kiprugut and was a metre in front. I was yelling to myself, 'I've won it, I've won it' and then I finally broke the tape. The moment was mine.

I was told that the noise in the Stadium during the race was at fever pitch. But I only heard silence. I didn't hear the crowd. I didn't see the crowd. I was immersed in my race for Gold.

After a few seconds with the race over, I rejoined the crowd in the Stadium. I could now hear the noise. I could see people. I waved to where I thought Franz was sitting. I asked Tom Farrell, who had come third, 'What is the world record for 800 metres?' He said that I had just equalled it. It was my day—in *my* Stadium…

But now we have a new Stadium in Sydney.

I've watched it being built. Marvelled at its grace. Delighted on how well it works. When asked to be a Director of Stadium Australia Management I immediately accepted. It rekindled memories of Mexico. The drawings provided inspiration. The financing plans were different and challenging—if only we knew then how challenging! And now it is finished and Sydney loves it.

In September and October next year Olympians and Paralympians will love it and will be inspired by it. After the Games they will look back and think the Stadium belongs to them. They will revisit it with their partners, parents and children and the Stadium will belong to them. But it will always belong to Sydney and it is yours.

This book shows how it developed. It shows the people who built it and the people who have enjoyed it. Alan Patching is one of those people. Few people know the Stadium as well as he does. Alan was critical in the development of the total concept. He could easily call it his Stadium. In this book he wants to share it with you. I hope you enjoy it.

MICHAEL KNIGHT

Minister for the Olympics

President, Sydney Organising Committee for the Olympic Games

Minister responsible for the Paralympic Games

Minister responsible for Darling Harbour

Since its first opening to the public in January of this year, Stadium Australia has fast become a new icon for Sydney and a sporting arena that will take Australian sport into the new millennium.

However, it is hard to imagine that only a little over two-and-a-half years ago the place where Stadium Australia now stands was a concrete slab with a faded Sydney 2000 Bid logo painted on it. And for most of the century before that it was the saleyards of the state's biggest abattoir.

As the New South Wales government minister responsible for oversighting the construction of the Stadium I am very proud of what has been achieved by Australian workers, designers, engineers and builders.

Of course, since its opening it has won the hearts of sports fans everywhere.

That's because it is a special place. It is a place where history will be made, great deeds will be done and triumph and tragedy will walk hand in hand. It is inspiration for all those who will compete there. And, between 18–29 October 2000 some of the world's greatest athletes will compete against each other for honour and glory in one of the most exciting sporting events ever held in this country—the Sydney 2000 Paralympic Games.

If it weren't for the Sydney 2000 Olympic Games, next year's Paralympic Games would be the largest sporting event held in Australia. Four thousand athletes from 125 countries will compete in 18 sports, making the Paralympics bigger than the 1998 Commonwealth Games or the 1988 Olympic Winter Games.

Having witnessed first-hand the glory, courage and humanity of Paralympic sport during the Atlanta Games I am sure that all Australians will become huge fans of the Paralympic Games.

I thank you for supporting the Paralympic Games by purchasing this history of Stadium Australia and I urge you to further support our great Paralympic athletes by cheering them to victory in October 2000.

Louise Sauvage OAM

Paralympic Gold Medallist

When I relocated from Perth to Sydney in 1997 I moved within a five-minute drive from the site of Stadium Australia.

On my first tour of the Homebush site, I became acquainted with the facilities that I would be using on a day-to-day basis as part of my training program and took in my first glimpse of the mound of dirt that was to be Stadium Australia.

Over the past two years, I have seen the Stadium rise to its now outstanding presence within the Olympic and Paralympic site. From week to week, construction progressed with the whole area taking on a new face. You could say the nightmare of the roads changing every few days made getting to training just a little more interesting.

Watching Stadium Australia grow was an exciting feeling—to think I live five minutes from the Olympic and Paralympic site!

Before the actual track surface was laid, I visited the Stadium and drove my car on to the area that is now recognised as the track. As construction went on around me I felt so insignificant in the centre with the 110 000 seating capacity surrounding me. That was an exciting and memorable day but the day that Joe and Bobbi Hoekstra invited me to the launch of the brand new 'Mondo' track was even more thrilling.

On this occasion, I arrived at Stadium Australia early and was one of the first athletes to go around the 'Mondo'-surfaced track, the first ever in Australia. I couldn't take the smile off my face, the track was just so fast.

I can only picture what it will be like in 2000, racing in Stadium Australia with a capacity crowd of Aussies screaming and cheering for all the Australian athletes.

Stadium Australia is a credit to all those involved with its design and construction. I have competed all over the world in many stadiums and at both Olympic and Paralympic Games, and Stadium Australia with its magnificent atmosphere is the essence of an ideal international sporting venue.

Louise Sauvage

The project director's diary

'And the winner is…Syd-en-ey.'

When International Olympic Committee President, Juan Antonio Samaranch, announced that the city had been chosen to be the venue for the Olympic Games in the year 2000, Sydney erupted into a marathon celebration. Across the city in bars and restaurants, on street corners, and in offices and homes, the shared celebrations fuelled a common theme of conversation: recognition for a job extremely well done by bid Chief Executive Rod McGeoch and his tireless and talented team.

The successful completion of the bid campaign heralded the commencement of another massive effort. Sydney needed to complete a multibillion infrastructure program in preparation for the Games of the 27th Olympiad. This program had to deliver first-class facilities within which the athletes of the world could push the benchmarks of sporting excellence. From an economic perspective, this infrastructure needed to serve as the base of Sydney's 'stage makeup' as she prepared to go under the spotlight of the Olympic Games when the press from all over the world would arrive in their thousands.

Most importantly, this infrastructure effort had to focus on the goal of endowing Sydney, and Australia,

with a post-Games legacy of facilities that would assist future generations of Australians in their quest to turn their wildest dreams of sporting achievement into reality. Sydney's Games legacy must afford the opportunity for talented Australian athletes to compete on a level footing with the world's best in a wide range of sporting endeavours well beyond 2000.

A prominent part of this legacy will be Stadium Australia, the Olympic Stadium. Like the Melbourne Cricket Ground of 1956 Olympics fame, the Stadium will surely become an Australian icon. This seems appropriate, given that sport has been such a dominant theme in our culture for so many decades.

Stadium Australia stands proudly at Homebush Bay. It is certainly the most prominent and, many would agree, the most important jewel in Sydney's outstanding Olympic facilities crown. The impressive dimensions and clean lines of the Stadium's sculptural design virtually guarantee that it will quickly become internationally recognised as a major symbol of Sydney and Australia.

The Stadium, with its 110 000 seats, is the largest ever constructed for an Olympic Games, the previous record holder being the 101 000-seat monster prepared in Los Angeles for the Games of the 23rd Olympiad, staged in 1984. Sydney's Olympic Stadium is a 'fourth generation' facility. Fourth generation means multi-functional and state of the art, including the flexibility to incorporate, with relative ease, the technical advances and commercial demands of the future. Stadium Australia has been designed to cater not only for major sporting events, but also for general commercial activity, ranging from simple parties or 'boardroom' lunches, to product launches and entertainment spectaculars.

However, the essential reason for the existence of this facility is to provide a stage for world-class performance in sport. The elite of rugby league christened the *StrathAyr* arena surface with a hugely successful first event and others, from all football codes and track-and-field athletics, will follow. These champions will be honoured and revered by the thousands of spectators at the events, as well as the millions watching on television around the world.

But these are not the only champions who should be recognised as part of the history of Stadium Australia.

Over 6000 people from 60 specialist consultancy firms and an equal number of construction subcontracting organisations provided their skills, under the construction management umbrella of Obayashi Corporation and Multiplex Constructions, to design and build Stadium Australia. In addition, teams of operators, underwriters, bankers, and financial, marketing and legal experts were involved. In total, around 6500 people from 60 different ethnic backgrounds, were part of the development, design and construction of Stadium Australia. Something in the order of three times that number participated in the manufacture and delivery of the materials used on the site. Many of this latter group may not even know of their contribution.

It is because of the enterprise and effort of these people that future generations of Australians will be able to witness and experience excellence in sporting performance for decades to come. They have demonstrated the extraordinary achievements human

beings are capable of when they strive together towards a common vision. These people were the first champions at Stadium Australia, and this book celebrates their magnificent effort.

Crossing the finish line: Building completion and the first event

It is 10.30 p.m. on Wednesday evening, 3 March 1999. Senior executives and legal advisers representing the contractors, the owning Stadium Australia Trust (SAT) and the Olympic Coordination Authority (OCA) are gathered in the boardroom of the Stadium administration offices on the third level of the western grandstand. Tension levels rise and tolerance levels fall as yet another

extension to an already too-long delay in proceedings is announced. We offer a glass of wine and a quick tour of the facility to pass the time, and this is quickly accepted. Nobody in the room wants the proceedings to extend a single second more, but all agree that no one will leave until a most important job is concluded.

The meeting began several hours earlier, in a mood of intense if understated excitement. It had been called for the owner, the SAT, to receive from the OCA a letter certifying that the building had reached a state of practical (effective) completion. This certification is a critical prerequisite for the staging of the first event, two rugby league matches, scheduled for just three days later.

This first event is a sellout, and so the people at the meeting are not the only ones in the Stadium Australia administration offices this evening. Management and operational staff with drawn faces and focused minds charge headlong into the final preparation for this very important Saturday evening. Many of these people, who work with the Stadium operators, Ogden International Facilities Corporation, and the Stadium caterer, Sodexho, have worked every day since Christmas, and the strain shows in their eyes. They are propelled by a clear realisation that this first event must be an unqualified success and, to a large extent, it is they who control its fate. As I dash between my office and the boardroom, they offer humour and encouragement, and inquire with genuine interest regarding progress. I know that somewhere deep within these dedicated people a part of them would not be disappointed if the answer was to be 'No certificate…Saturday's off…go home'. But such a thought is untenable, the show must go on, and tonight's all-important formalities must be concluded successfully.

The challenge causing the delay arises from a contractual provision that the certificate cannot be issued until the bank providing the project finance gives its consent. The letter of consent the bank has provided is not satisfactory to the lawyers representing the other parties, including us. It seems to the non-lawyers among us that we are witnessing the greatest demonstration of nitpicking in the history of property development. The lawyers convince us that the debate is necessary.

I find humour in a private reflection that, as our group applies its collective intellect to seeking a solution, nearly 110 000 sports lovers, oblivious to our problem, are calling babysitters, checking transport schedules and taking one more look at their tickets, in final preparation for a very special night at the footy. The consequences of not successfully concluding the business at hand within the next 48 hours, and preferably this evening, are too enormous to entertain. How would one go about advising the ticket holders that they could not attend the

games? How would one advise the Board of the National Rugby League that the opening event of their season could not proceed at Stadium Australia? With a State election only three weeks away, what effect would a cancellation have at the ballot box?

MTM Stadium Management Limited (MTM) Chairman, Stephen Rix, and I have spent the past couple of hours negotiating with the bank and its advisers, frequently visiting the boardroom to deliver updates. Faces brighten each time we appear, only to express deeper disappointment as our latest news is delivered and absorbed.

Minor changes are made to the letter by the bank in Melbourne, and the fax comes to life to deliver it to our office at an irritatingly leisurely pace. We all return to the

boardroom, check the document and nod approval. The conditions prerequisite to certification have been met. Olympic Coordination Authority Director of Stadia, Paul Gilbertson, hands me the Certificate of Practical Completion. I look at my watch. I notice that it is precisely 32 minutes and 27 seconds after eleven.

The piece of paper in my hands is the most important of the thousands of letters generated during the previous 30 months of the design and construction period. More than any other milestone in the project's development, receipt of the Certificate of Completion is cause for serious celebration. Despite this, we all head home. There is no time for even a single celebratory drink. There remain less than three days to the first event. In this time a construction site must be converted into an inviting and effectively functioning venue. The task of removing builders' sheds and completing the site clean-up is substantial. Equally substantial is the job of delivering 2500 kegs of beer and hundreds of truckloads of food and catering utensils, and distributing their contents throughout the building.

Thursday and Friday are similarly intense days. Ninety cleaners from the operations team complete the final clean-up of the areas that will be occupied by the public, while the Multiplex cleaning team focus on the basement service areas. Ogden's Richard Knight and his team are the people who will run the Stadium during the big event. They have experience with other substantial venues, and they know where the problems are likely to arise. We agree that they should prepare a list of current concerns and continually update and prioritise the items on it.

Ron Kofoed, Multiplex's director for the project, agrees that the already cooperative relationship between his people and ours must be elevated to even greater heights. He commits his personnel to focus on first-event preparation above all else.

Meetings are held each day with Multiplex's construction management people and the operators' senior staff. Problem areas are assessed one by one. At the end of each day, an inspection crew walks the entire facility, checking progress on items identified for action, and noting other areas in need of urgent attention. The builders' sheds have gone from the basement. Tick. But now there is the issue of cleaning where they were. Note. The gap adjacent to the exit gates has been rectified. Tick. But what about that final rehearsal for the personnel who would manage the exit gates in an emergency? High priority; how about first thing tomorrow morning? We find a small piece of metal on the roof catwalk. No telling what damage that could do to a human skull if it managed to fall through the

walkway mesh. One final check is necessary. Tick.

After a couple of early bugs, the system works effectively.

Things are also going well in the temporary staff administration area in the basement service level. Most of the brightly coloured uniforms for casual staff and all of the fulltime personnel outfits have been fitted, adjusted and issued. Representatives of Neat 'n Trim, the designers and manufacturers of the uniforms, are pleased. They have delivered on all of their undertakings and the job is now done to the approval of staff and spectators. The smiles on the faces of Dawn Carroll of Multiplex and Nicole Uren from MTM, key people in managing the purchase of all uniforms and each piece of the several million dollars worth of furniture and equipment in the facility, tell of their satisfaction with the achievement.

Chris Chapman, CEO of Stadium Australia Management (SAM), and Ken Edwards, Managing Director of Ogden, advise me that Sodexho, the

catering contractor (and an equity holder) for Stadium Australia have some concerns about the state of readiness of kitchens and cooking facilities. Although Mike Lonergan, the Multiplex operative who was appointed as project manager to Sodexho for this work, disagrees with this assessment, we cannot risk problems with food delivery for the first, or any, event. Stephen Rix and I decide to examine the alleged problem areas first hand. Richard Errington, Sodexho's on-site manager, and Lonergan join us.

'Truck access to storage areas is obstructed by site sheds.' (Errington)

'Yes, also by catering staff parking too close; the sheds'll be gone tomorrow.' (Lonergan)

Point by point the issues are examined, discussed and dealt with.

Dieter Grun, Sodexho's highly respected ex-Hayman Island executive chef, expresses serious concern with technical problems in food and drink outlets. A gas line not connected here, an entire area not yet commissioned there. A troubleshooting team of project managers and technical specialists is appointed to visit every one of the approximately 90 food outlets and bars throughout the Stadium. Every switch is activated, every supply point operated, every drain inspected and every piece of equipment tested.

The firms and people associated with the venue are well aware that their reputation is on the line for this first event. We sense a pervading commitment to a first-class outcome, and this is evident in the levels of cooperation throughout the Stadium. Things that need to get done simply get done, and no one stalls in debate over minor issues.

We're going to make it! It *will* be right on the night!

Stadium Australia opens its door: The first event

It is 3.03 p.m. on Saturday, 6 March 1999. A simple, even-voiced, matter-of-fact announcement is made over Stadium Australia's public address system: 'Open the shutters'. There is a roar from the patrons queuing and strolling in the precinct.

Stadium Australia is open for business.

The customer service personnel are as excited as the spectators, and the atmosphere quickly begins to build. Finding seats proves a challenge for some, but no one is upset. There is too much to see en route to be overly concerned about problems with the journey.

By the time spectators reach their allocated seats, they are understandably in awe of the features, scale and design of Australia's newest sporting venue. By the time

they leave their seats, they are blown away by the experience they have been part of. The National Rugby League's Newcastle Knights, Manly Sea Eagles, Parramatta Eels and St George Illawarra Dragons provide the gladiatorial action, with the Knights and the Eels registering victories over the Sea Eagles and the Dragons respectively. The sporting spectacular is outstanding. Listening to 104 853 people expressing appreciation for skilful footy play makes it easy to imagine being present at the 2000 Olympic Games when 110 000 people respond spontaneously to Cathy Freeman or one of her team mates smashing a world record.

The big fellows are not the only attraction of the evening. Hundreds of junior players, spurred on by families in the crowd, are actually the first to play

football on what will surely become the hallowed turf of the arena. And a children's choir wins more attention and enthusiasm from the crowds than the organisers could have imagined or hoped for.

After a couple of false starts, a Mexican wave circumnavigates the ground. It may not be the best the world has ever seen, but what it lacks in precision it certainly makes up for in enthusiasm.

When each patron arrives at his or her seat, they find a plastic bag containing a red or blue-green 'Cyalume' light stick. These sticks are designed to be broken to activate a coloured glow at the time the ground announcer asks the crowd to 'light up Stadium Australia'—part of an EnergyAustralia promotion. But the curiosity is too compelling, and sticks are broken soon after the patrons arrive, converting the seating areas into a sea of moving fairy lights. The sight is spectacular.

To be at Stadium Australia this evening is to be part of something very, very special.

Transport

Transport, thought to be one area where problems could arise on the night, is a hot topic for discussion among the crowd, and we are interested in the opinions expressed. Most reports are of a public transport system that works brilliantly. Extra trains are scheduled, shuttle buses operate between the site and temporary car parks established at shopping centres near the Stadium, and some 300 private buses are engaged to transport patrons and players. The precinct near the Stadium is designed with some 170 bus parking bays and, for this event, the OCA has established extra temporary parking bays within its extensive site area. Parking positions are marked with large illuminated, numbered balls to assist patrons in finding their way back to their 'chariots' after the event.

Behind the scenes

While all is going well in the seating bowl and the public spaces, the event management two-way radio crackles incessantly with reports of happenings behind the scenes. Most of the banter is routine, but some areas are of concern and one or two warn of possible crises.

A grease-trap in a fast-food outlet develops a fault, and gallons of slimy goo oozes out over the main concourse under the northern grandstand. This is definitely a risk to patrons and requires urgent attention. The matter is reported to the event control room and, within minutes, a team is sent to cordon off the area and distribute sand over the spillage. Police officers ensure that patrons remain clear of the area. It

is a problem we could have done without, and a food outlet is closed for the rest of the evening. On the positive side, it is comforting to know that the emergency management system has passed its first live test promptly and effectively.

A gas leak is reported on the upper level of the southern stand. This one is crucial, and could necessitate a partial evacuation. Tom Stringer of Ogden is patrolling in the basement. He and others are quickly on the scene. Tense voices relax as the inspection team determines that the leak is in the beverage gas system, which 'puts the bubbles in the beer', and is not from the fuel gas supply lines. There is no danger to patrons.

Throughout the evening, Ogden's Darryl Kerry, already tired from long hours over the last couple of days, controls the event with his enthusiastic team from a small fifth-level room with a panoramic view of the entire seating bowl and arena. He reminds me of a triage manager at an emergency hospital. All problems are reported direct to Darryl, who disperses inspection

teams, considers reports and prioritises issues within an action list. Darryl is ice-cool under pressure, with the perfect radio voice and manner for the job—a mix of confident authority and calming reassurance. At the end of the evening, I visit Darryl in the event control centre. He is lying back in his chair, arms dangling over the arm rests. His eyes are red and his voice lacks energy. He manages a grateful smile when I tell him that, in nearly 35 years in the property business, I have never seen a better demonstration of property operation. I mean it.

Earlier, a routine walk around the basement service area with Chris Chapman reveals a generally busy scene punctuated by groups of workers chatting during their break and the occasional group of colourful cheer-squad members having their important evening photographed. We are satisfied that the basement service area design concept is working extremely well, with vehicles travelling right to the doors of storage areas to unload their cargo. The design of this area was the subject of a long and, at times, heated debate during the development period. Olympic Coordination Authority officers were advised on design issues by an architectural firm resident in the USA. This firm advocated the adoption of the US system of a central loading dock at the entrance to the facility, with stadium staff transporting unloaded goods to their final storage position. It was a system driven by a level of concern over security that we did not believe to be justified in Australia – certainly not to the extent that it should dictate the design of the all-important service level of the building. The clockwork operation of the service level leading up to the first event and over the ensuing weeks satisfies all involved that the debate was worthwhile.

Back in the arena, the formalities stage is now set up in centre field. Football stars are introduced along with legends from many other sports. Following this, sprint sensation Matt Shirvington, the fastest white man the world has seen, visualises what it would be like to win an Olympic sprint medal in front of a capacity crowd at this venue. Maybe, just maybe, the Stadium Australia team has managed to inspire the great to an even higher excellence in performance. And maybe, our deeper, but nonetheless clearly identified goal of creating a venue that does not simply accommodate sporting events, but rather inspires extraordinary achievement by athletes, will be realised.

The talented singing group, Human Nature, obliges the crowd with an energetic performance. I smile as I note that they were just as obliging, when, the previous day, not having a clue who they were, I asked them to refrain from disturbing the arena turf during some goal-kicking fun. Their football skills may be a little wanting,

but they certainly score hugely with the crowd during this opening event performance.

Australian singing sensation, Marcia Hines is also at her best, thrilling the already excited crowd. She is followed by a spectacular laser show, and a fireworks display—awesome, despite the considerable damage it did to the high tech roof sheeting; something to take into account at future events.

I am impressed but not significantly moved by all of the fantastic happenings in the arena. Perhaps I am distracted by a secret wish to have the event successfully concluded. This will effectively signal that the long and demanding design and construction effort has achieved its goals. My thoughts are interrupted as Genevieve Davies takes the centre stage and, after a false start caused by a faulty microphone switch, begins singing the national anthem. She is soon joined by 104 853 proud Australians. The atmosphere is now electric. The sound of the crowd is indescribable. The experience is spine-chilling.

I have never been more proud of a career achievement than I am at that moment, and the eyes of those around me express similar emotion. Stadium Australia Management Chairman, Paul Isherwood, is sporting a smile of relief that's as eye-catching as his bow tie. Stadium Australia Management Limited board member, Ralph Doubell, is standing with our group. He is the 800-metres gold medallist from the 1968 Mexico Olympics, and is one of the coolest characters I have ever met. This evening, at this moment, the ice has melted, and there is a tear of pride in Doubell's eye. Perhaps, mid-evening in Sydney on 6 March 1999, he is reliving his great moment in Mexico. Or perhaps he, like everyone involved in the making of Stadium Australia, realises that we have created something extraordinary here, and is simply expressing deep-felt satisfaction with his part in that achievement.

The first event at Stadium Australia opened its page in the annals of Australian and world sporting history. All who were involved in its creation will treasure the future moments as that page is expanded.

The membership scheme

Soon after the gates open for the first event, Stephen Rix and I conduct an inspection tour of all members' facilities. Chris Chapman and Ken Edwards conduct similar inspections, as members are a very important part of the Stadium Australia story. Platinum and Gold Members, equipped with knowledge gained from attending open days during the construction period, are quick to find their way to their impressively appointed restaurants, lounges and bars. We agree that members' faces seem to express their satisfaction with their investment.

There are 600 Platinum Members, and each paid $34 000 for the privilege of membership, contributing a total of over $20 million in equity funds. For this they are entitled to attend every sporting event and to bring a guest free of charge to every non-Olympic event for the entire 31 years that Stadium Australia Trust owns the Stadium. Platinum Members also get tickets to every Stadium event of the Olympic Games at no extra cost. Parking is provided and they pay no annual membership fee. The Platinum Members' Lounge and padded arena seating is located in the western stand on the fifth level. The dining and lounge facilities are the best in the venue and the arena seating commands fabulous views of the playing field.

Gold members paid $10 000 and a nominal yearly membership fee, and also get free tickets to every Olympic and non-Olympic sporting event held at the Stadium. They are not entitled to bring guests for free

but can bid to bring up to three guests at normal event ticket prices where seating is available for non-Olympic events, and these guests are entitled to use the members facilities. These facilities include well-appointed lounges on the second and fourth levels of the western grandstand, and a light and spacious two-storey lounge bar, bistro dining and fine dining restaurants on the fourth level. Car parking is not included in the Gold Members deal.

The original financial plan allowed for 34 400 Gold Memberships which would raise $344 million in equity, and these were to be sold by way of a public float. Unfortunately the float did not meet expectations, with

only 11 000 sales being made. The response was quite the opposite for the Platinum Membership, where there was significantly more demand than there were memberships available. The Platinum Membership reads like a 'who's who' of Sydney business.

The experts agreed that one significant reason for the shortfall in Gold Membership sales was that the prospectus was too technical. Notwithstanding the problems with the float, it was fully underwritten and raised $364 million in equity for the project.

The unsold Gold Memberships created the opportunity to establish a 'code membership' arrangement. Under this scheme, 17 200 Gold Memberships were effectively bought back from the underwriters and were dedicated for use as 'code memberships'. The Stadium Gold Membership is given the exclusive use of the prime seating areas and club facilities in the western stand, while the club facilities and prime seating areas in the eastern stand are reserved for the codes (and their membership) hiring the venue.

The design and construction phase

Stadium Australia was probably the country's largest project during the time of its design and construction. The function which gives reason for its very existence—

its use as the main venue for the opening and closing ceremonies, the soccer final and the track-and-field events of the 27th Olympic Games—ensures a heightened public interest in the Stadium. Certainly it was the project with the highest profile in the country. It is of immense credit to everyone involved in the design and construction process that the Stadium was completed on time and to budget. The contractors claimed not a single day's extension. The only cost extras were those that received owner's approval before proceeding, and all of these were completed without an increase to the original budget.

Apart from membership holders, there are several equity partners in the project, and many of these have an ongoing role in the operation of the Stadium. Understandably, their input during the design and construction stage often seemed to be inspired as much by a desire to protect their investment as it was by an empathy with the essential long-term interests of the project ownership.

This had a number of minor consequences during the design and construction period, not the least being that the owner's project management team had to be more than doubled to ensure that issues raised received due attention and were debated to their conclusion. On the very few occasions that I had to make a decision

that did not entirely meet the needs of a particular party, this process generated sufficient satisfaction to allow matters to continue without further challenge.

The public's interest in the project was safeguarded by the involvement of the OCA. Given the high profile of the project, and in the interests of an open approach in the process of delivering it, MTM agreed to a level of OCA involvement well in excess of the dictates of the formal contractual arrangements. For example, the contracts required some 200 meetings involving the OCA during the course of the project. In total, we welcomed the OCA's attendance at in excess of 1300 meetings.

A dual-level approach to project communication was adopted. At what was called the 'conversational' level, any person from any of the parties involved could

exchange information with any other person. However, the only manner in which change could be formalised, schedules altered, or budgets adjusted in any way was through formal contractual channels, which we referred to as the 'instructional' communication lines.

Without doubt, this open approach to the project's management substantially contributed to the fact that the OCA never pursued a single formal notice of non-compliance during the entire design and construction process.

Completion of the Stadium on schedule was achieved despite an environment of detailed and sometimes protracted debate on even the most minor design issues. This would not have been realised without the high level of program flexibility and tolerance the contractors demonstrated. This flexibility even allowed for several million dollars worth of extra structural work to be incorporated without an extension of the schedule, despite this occurring near to program deadlines. Some of this structural work was required to ensure that Australian Rules Football will be played at Stadium Australia after the Games. For those involved in the negotiations for the inclusion of Australian Rules, it is difficult now to imagine that the project could ever reach its highest potential without all football codes being catered for.

My MTM colleague, Nicole Uren, coordinated our cost control for the Stadium and this was feasibility based, as I believe it should be for all major projects. There were a number of changes made to enhance the initial design with which the Stadium Australia Group won the right to finance, design, construct, operate and maintain the project until 2031.

For example, the contract brief called for a number of corporate suites of a defined size and in a specific location, serviced by a system wherein food was prepared in a commissary kitchen in the basement, and finished off in four serveries adjacent to the suites, two in each of the east and west grandstands. The group's business plan identified corporate facilities as the major single source of income in the facility. It seemed wise to improve these in any way that was reasonably possible. After a long period of vigorous investigation and debate on the issue, it was decided to increase the length of the suites, to build in a kitchenette/servery for every two standard suites, and to incorporate the structural ability to make some of the suites flexible in width. These changes were seen to enhance the likelihood of a greater return in the long term from the corporate suites and so were definitely considered a worthwhile investment.

This approach of evaluating the likely return of every suggested design alteration before proceeding to commit

funds to it was standard procedure throughout the project. Even then, we did not proceed with a suggested change until a confirmed price was received from the contractor and a feasibility check and/or value engineering* exercise assured us that funds were available to pay for the work. Using this approach we were able to achieve design enhancements worth several million dollars without exceeding the original budget.

Conservation initiatives

The Games of the 27th Olympiad have been nicknamed 'The Green Games', due to the emphasis placed on environmental issues. The design for Stadium Australia responds to several environmental design imperatives, showing particular sensitivity to environmental matters in a number of areas.

* Value engineering involves reviewing the design solution for the functional requirements of the project to determine if a less expensive solution would do the job and free up already allocated funds for use in other areas.

Passive ventilation system

There is less airconditioning in Stadium Australia than one would expect in a facility of this type. Most areas are passively ventilated. This simply means that, where possible, natural air movement is encouraged through the building as an integral part of the complete ventilation system. Certain areas of the ground-level concourses, for example, use this passive ventilation system. In areas where natural air movement is not always appropriate—such as spaces largely enclosed by concrete walls and floors—a system of ducting and fans is used to direct the flow of natural air. An example of this is in the club members lounges on the fourth level of each of the east and west grandstands. In yet other areas a combined system is installed, with the passive system being operated in all circumstances, except where it is not capable of lowering the temperature below a certain preordained level. Once this temperature mark is passed, a standard airconditioning system takes over the ventilation task. This system typically is employed in the larger dining and conference spaces with an exposure to an external wall, such as the fourth-level banquet rooms.

Rainwater collection system

Rainwater is collected from the roof and stored in four

large storage tanks, one in each corner of the basement. Each tank holds 800 cubic metres of water and this is used to irrigate the arena, thus reducing demand on the city's potable water supplies.

Use of natural lighting

The use of natural light is maximised throughout the building to reduce demand on the city's power supply grid. The main escalator void on either side of the building also serves as a light well, with light reflected down the void from the whitened underside of the upper-seating tier, and distributed onto floors through glass brick walls. The perforated sunshades of the banquet halls restrict entry of direct sunlight while at the same time allowing maximum natural light to enter the spaces. The offices on the third level of each of the east and west grandstands are shaded from direct sun by the overhanging floors of the banquet halls above, while still being provided with a very high level of natural light. Office partitions parallel to the external walls are made of glass to further enhance the distribution of this natural light throughout the office space.

Use of PVC

There is a greatly reduced use of PVC materials throughout the building compared with what one might

expect in a building of this size and type. For example, 60 per cent of the electrical cabling is of non-PVC material and no PVC flooring is used in the facility.

Power generation

Gas fired equipment is used to generate power within the Stadium and this minimises demand on the grid supply.

Garbage disposal

The entire garbage disposal system within Stadium Australia has been designed to comply with the highest standards of waste separation and to maximise the potential for recycling of waste materials.

'Green' initiatives were also employed during

construction. All waste was separated, categorised and appropriately disposed of during the construction period and, to ensure maximum compliance, site workers were given training in environmental matters as part of Multiplex's site induction training course. In addition, the dirt road around the external perimeter of the facility was constantly watered to prevent dust polluting the air. Water used for this was collected on-site and stored in one of the basement storage tanks. Up to 50 000 litres of water was used per day for this task.

Other design features

Seating design

With the impact it would inevitably have on the overall look of the Stadium, the design of the arena seating was always going to be an interesting exercise. The contracts clearly established the final decision to be the owner's responsibility, and that meant I would be the one in the line of fire. I decided on an approach of open discussion and debate. Multiplex and its architects submitted five designs for consideration, and it took only a day or so for all parties to narrow the range of possibilities down to two. One was a pixilated design, whereby the seats would be in a palette of colours, arranged in a computer-generated pattern intended to reduce the television viewer's awareness of empty seating during events attracting smaller crowds.

The second short-listed design was the 'first cut' of the design that was eventually chosen. Changes were made to the colour of the mid-tier seats, and the logo used during the Sydney bid campaign was included in the seating layout to the upper levels of the temporary end stands. Chris Chapman suggested that we ask the designers to investigate the inclusion of the logo in its original colours, but this turned out to be a harder task than any of us had imagined. The consensus eventually fell on the two-tone blue wave pattern, which is now a much-admired feature of the Stadium.

I must admit that my first preference was for the pixilated design. However, I did not see the alternative as in any way disappointing, and so I went with the flow of the agreed majority. I'm glad I did. The seat colours look brilliant, and I doubt that anyone could now convince me that the pixilated design could look better. Come to think of it, no one has ever tried!

There exists a project legend that the seating design was inspired when, during a few drinks one evening, one of the architects noticed a fellow drinker's necktie and exclaimed that he had found the inspiration he had been looking for. One would hope that the formal explanation—that the pattern was inspired by the waters surrounding Sydney and by the other curvo-linear

aspects of the Stadium's design—lies closer to the truth of the matter.

This, however, was not the only legend to emerge from the development of Stadium Australia. One of the best focuses on the roof design.

The Stadium roof

The design of Stadium Australia's roof was a complex exercise. This complexity gave rise to the opportunity for a bit of fun. One of Multiplex's designers, in a larrikin mood during a very serious presentation, stated that the concept of 'pringaleon geometry' was used in the design of the roof structure. There were some very red faces seen on some very experienced professionals when our

designer friends eventually exposed the 'concept' as a gag. A major newspaper ran an article explaining that the term was a light-hearted reference to the fact that the roof design very much resembled the shape of a 'Pringle' potato chip. The company which produces the Pringle chips was quick to see an opportunity, running an advertisement expressing its pride in providing the source of inspiration for this very important aspect of Stadium Australia's design.

The story of the erection of the amazing arched roof structure is told, with a series of photographs, elsewhere in this book. However, there is more to the roof technology than its structural support system. Early in 1999, sports lovers the world over sat glued to their television sets as the matches of the FIFA soccer World Cup were played out in Paris. The French team eventually claimed victory in their newest sporting venue, the Stade de France. The roof is one of the prominent design features of this wonderful facility, and it received much praise from the hundreds of commentators and journalists covering the event. Several saw it as a technical marvel.

I remember suppressing a grin during a presentation by the design engineer for Stadium Australia, Steve Morley of Modus Engineering, at an international conference on stadia held in Cardiff, Wales, in 1998.

Steve explained to an enthralled audience that the high-tech roof of the Stade de France weighed around 200 kilograms per square metre, while the very high-tech roof on Stadium Australia weighed a mere 60 kilograms (approximately) per square metre. Everyone seemed impressed, except, understandably, for one or two of the French delegates!

The roof is a significant element of Stadium Australia's easily recognised aesthetics. It is also an outstanding functional feature of the Stadium design. It covers some 65 per cent of the arena seating pre-Olympics and around 80 per cent following post-Olympic construction works which will add a roof at each end and reduce the seating capacity to 80 000. Its lightweight polycarbonate sheeting provides sound insulation and sun protection while allowing transmission of up to 48 per cent of incident light. This accounts for less contrast between lighted and in-shadow portions of the playing surface, a great attraction to television producers.

The catering fitout

Many would consider a sporting venue to comprise little more than the playing arena and seating. Indeed, this description would have been reasonably accurate not so many years ago. However, it most certainly is not the case for multi-functional venues such as Stadium

Australia. Apart from some 40 arena events each year, a business plan including several hundred conferences, dinners and other functions demands a high-tech, state-of-the-art catering fitout. For this reason, Sodexho has installed kitchen equipment valued at well over $20 million. Put in perspective, this means that the Stadium has catering equipment the equivalent of several of Sydney's five star hotels combined.

In addition, there is over 50 kilometres of tubing installed within the Stadium to distribute the beverages supplied by Coca Cola and Tooheys and the BOC gases that carbonate these beverages and deliver them through the tubes to the point of sale.

The catering fitout was a major consideration

throughout the design and construction process. Literally hundreds of meetings were held to discuss in detail every aspect of this most important component of the Stadium's infrastructure. Senior personnel from the fields of architecture, services engineering, kitchen design, catering, construction and project management debated even the most minor issues to resolution over many months. When the executive chef was appointed, the entire design underwent a further review despite construction of the catering fitout being well advanced. The entire process was sometimes tedious and frustrating, but no one ever lost sight of its absolute importance. The final product of this effort is proof that, on this occasion at least, 'too many cooks did not spoil the broth'.

As is the case in so many high-pressure situations, humour was the glue that kept the process on track. One example that quickly comes to mind involved Sodexho's general manager of catering, Richard Errington, contributing to a general design discussion. Responding to an architect's statement that it looked like all things had been considered at a particular point of the design process, Errington commented that the excitement of big footy matches took the ultimate toll on some patrons at other venues he had been involved with. Based on this experience, he considered that we would be well advised to install a small morgue facility. No sooner had he offered this contribution than some wag interjected, 'Why, is the food really going to be that bad?'

Projects like this need lots of humorous moments like that. Fortunately, there was no shortage of them during the design and construction of Stadium Australia.

The world's largest railway carriages

The original design for Stadium Australia did not contemplate the playing of oval field sports post-Olympics. The key reason for this is that spectators like to enjoy intimacy with the action, and to design an oval field around 170 metres long and 130 metres wide means that patrons of rectangular field sports (typically 100 metres by 70 metres) are a long way from the action.

After commencement of construction, the senior executives of MTM, SAM, and Multiplex revisited the prospect of Australian Rules football being played at Stadium Australia. With the design well advanced, it really did not seem like a strong possibility. However, everyone in the senior team passionately believed that it would be a great bonus to have 'Aussie Rules' included in the future agenda and committed themselves to finding a way to ensure that this occurred. The executives of the OCA were completely supportive of our goal, and the Australian Football League (AFL) also

expressed great interest in the prospect.

We realised that there was one way we could include Australian Rules in our future games agenda. Effectively, this would involve converting a large area of the lower seating bowl of the east and west grandstands to 'the world's largest railway carriages'. We would need to move a huge piece of structure holding 47 rows of seating about 95 metres long on either side of the arena inwards 15 metres for rectangular field events, and back for oval field events. This could be done in one of several methods, but a railway system was the most appealing. The tracks will be installed under where the Olympic track now lies and covered with 'sod pans' containing turf when the seats are in the rear position. The wheels will be railway type and will be driven by computer-controlled motors. When the structure moves forward, bridges will be erected between the concourse and the seats. The entire transformation occurs in the space of 6 to 8 hours.

With construction progressing rapidly, decisions had

to be made quickly. The first was to ensure that the footings being constructed at the time would be capable of supporting any additional structure necessary to allow for an Australian Rules configuration in the future. Multiplex and its designers got to work and determined that spending just over $1 million would keep our options open. This amount was funded by contribution from the AFL and the New South Wales government. It was with a great sense of joy that I wrote the instruction for the 'AFL Futureproofing' work, as it became known, to proceed. The contractors included the extra work in their schedule without any delay to the completion schedule.

This step bought us time to investigate in detail just how the remainder of the design would need to be changed for the inclusion of Aussie Rules. Ed Obiala, Multiplex's construction manager, is a man with an interesting life history, an encyclopaedic knowledge of athletes and athletics, a brilliant mind for engineering and a passion for the Olympics. Ed was the ideal construction manager for Stadium Australia. The designers he keenly orchestrates to complete the investigation into the technical feasibility use computer-based design and analysis systems far removed from the 'kerosene lamp' technology with which Ed studied for his university degree in Poland over thirty years ago. At the same time as the boffins are at work, Chris Chapman of SAM, and Ken Edwards and his team from Ogden, busy themselves in the commercial research we will need to make the final decision.

The outcome—it is technically feasible to construct the Stadium to cater for both rectangular and oval field sports, but we will need a greater game commitment from the AFL than was earlier anticipated. By this time, construction has progressed to the point where an immediate decision is needed regarding upgrading of major structural elements, such as columns and lower level floor slabs, to allow the movement that is an essential prerequisite for AFL being played. This time the sourcing of the funds will not be an easy task. We will need nearly $6 million.

Multiplex, in addition to being the main contractor (under head contractor, Obayashi Corporation) for the project, it is also the largest shareholder in the venture. Its commitment to the project was clearly evident when it agreed to provide loan funds to ensure that all pre-Olympic structural work necessary to allow the playing of Aussie Rules post-Olympics, is completed. At the time of writing, the AFL has committed to a match schedule sufficient to proceed with the dream. The $23.5 million AFL works will be completed between the end of the Paralympics and the beginning of the 2002 football

season. Sufficient work will be completed by March 2001 to allow AFL matches to be played during that season. Arrangements between SAT, the ANZ Bank, the New South Wales government and the AFL will assist in financing the project.

I will have immense satisfaction, on behalf of all involved in the very intricate and time-consuming negotiations behind this very important deal, in issuing the formal instruction for the work to proceed. The Multiplex site team, will derive the same level of satisfaction from delivering the goods. And thousands of Australians visiting Stadium Australia, for decades to come, will enjoy the high-flying athletes of the AFL.

The great Stadium Australia toilet flush

Late in the construction phase, we were keen to comply with a contractual requirement that the entire sanitary installation be tested under maximum load conditions.

Given that the first event was likely to be a sell-out, we needed to ensure that the drainage lines were not being obstructed with construction debris, a common occurrence on major projects. The designers of the system confirmed that it was capable of handling simultaneous flushing of all units in the installation, but we did not want to face the embarrassment of finding out on the big night that the designers were wrong. Also, we wanted the comfort of knowing that the city could provide sufficient water pressure to recharge all of the cisterns in a short period of time, and simultaneously.

There was only one way to be sure of all of these things. Just before noon on a bright Saturday morning a week or so before completion, several hundred casual Stadium staff were joined by over a hundred more volunteers from the OCA and its consultants in the banquet room on the fourth level of the east grandstand. There they received a briefing from yours truly in preparation for a most important event—the great Stadium Australia toilet flush. Every toilet and urinal in the facility, some 1125 of the former and 300 of the latter, would be flushed simultaneously three times, at intervals of one minute. The briefing was, of course, a very serious affair, but the group nonetheless responded with vivid imagination to the potential unpleasant consequences of any major hiccup in the working of the least mentioned but most important system in the facility.

The exercise was completed along organisation lines borrowed from the military, with a 'general' nominated for each grandstand. In turn, 'captains' were appointed for each level within each grandstand, 'lieutenants' for specific areas within each level, and so on. Finally, groups of people commensurate with the number of fittings in each toilet area, were appointed from those gathered in the banquet hall to the individuals ultimately responsible for these areas. The reason for the structured breakup of resources was the need to communicate via two-way radio as well as over the public address system (to cover any situation wherein the public address could not be heard) to ensure simultaneous operation of all cisterns.

I managed the operation from the event control room on the fifth level, giving regular updates of progress to those already in position as others moved to more distant toilet blocks. I hate being delayed on aircraft without an explanation, and I did not want our volunteers to face that type of frustration. Colin Ging and his project management team from the OCA assisted in the management of the operation.

The event was a huge success and a lot of fun. Only a few minor problems were detected in the sewerage and water supply systems, and the sense of involvement and camaraderie the exercise engendered among all manner

of people from any number of positions in the large number of contractual and employment arrangements with the Stadium Australia Group was valuable. It was humorous to see this often taboo subject become the bonding force between so many people. A local television channel made the most of the sandwich lunch that followed the event, recording animated reports from enthusiastic participants in this simple but important event in the development of the Stadium—one that I am sure will be remembered and recounted with affection to generations of future Australians.

The Greek connection

One of the merchant bankers associated with Stadium Australia is of Greek extraction. He happened to be a close friend of one of the construction supervisors. Just prior to construction of the arena, these two took a tiny pebble 'borrowed' from the site of the first ever Olympic Stadium in Greece, and placed it in a small container,

along with a current Greek coin and one from Australia. They wrote a few lines and buried the container beneath the arena surface, a symbol of the first ever Olympics and the last of this millennium (or first, depending on whether or not they were one of the many who cannot understand the fuss about 1 January 2000, given that 1 January 2001 signifies the commencement of the third millennium).

The merchant banker then suggested to a group of senior Stadium Australia Group executives that it would be appropriate to approach the Greek government with a view to having a more substantial token exhibited in the Stadium. Chris Chapman, CEO of SAM, pursued the matter with the Greek authorities. As a result, displayed proudly in the main entrance foyer of the western grandstand is an impressive slab of granite taken from the same Mt Olympus quarry as was the granite used in construction of the stadium at which were played the very first Olympic Games. This is a marvelous gesture on behalf of the Greek people, who diligently guard their national treasures with understandable jealousy.

In conclusion

With the passing of time and continuing improvement in technology at all levels, the Stadium Australia design and construction experience might one day be seen as little more than a series of simple exercises, despite the fact that each of these exercises was incredibly complex in itself. Moving several hundred thousand cubic metres of earth to level the site, or drilling and constructing 2600 piles, or even moulding 20 000 truckloads of concrete and several thousand tonnes of steel into the sculptural form that is Stadium Australia, might never command long chapters in the history books, but these activities will never be erased from the minds of those involved. And if the traditional Australian values of hard work and dedication to achieve a goal that prevailed in the design offices and on the site extend among the participants to other values—the ones that have proud grandparents reliving inspirational career experiences to wide-eyed grandchildren sitting on their knees—the story behind the manifestation of the Stadium Australia dream will never die.

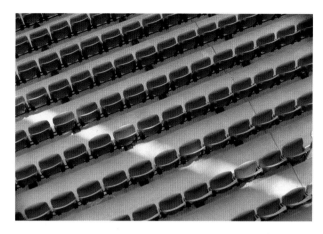

But the manifestation of a single dream is not what Stadium Australia represents. Six-thousand-and-five-hundred people endured and enjoyed a sometimes frustrating, often arduous, always exciting design and construction phase to be part of the thirty-month gestation of one dream. Each person valued being a part of something very special, being a part of history in the making. I often sat in the highest parts of the structure during construction in the early evening after most of the construction workers had left. I found this to be a highly spiritual experience, the cathedral silence in those lofty heights was quite inspirational. It was here that I often

thought about the importance of the effort of the 6500. After all, they produced the field upon which thousands of athletes will channel years of intense training into a few minutes—just a few seconds for many—of peak performance which might well dictate their life's direction for decades thereafter.

My own prayer is that those who achieve their highest aspirations on this field of dreams will inspire my children and their children, and children from every corner of the world, by their performance and so motivate them to spread their own wings and soar to heights of achievement in their chosen endeavours that they might otherwise never have believed possible. This is more than my prayer, it is my own dream of Stadium Australia, and it is a dream that has made every second of my personal involvement on the project well worth the effort.

Early history

An aerial view of the abattoir that once occupied the Olympic site at Homebush. (photo provided by Fred McDonald)

The Stadium site began its life (in the 'European' system) when a grant was made in 1810 to D'Arcy Wentworth, who was an assistant surgeon. The 370 hectare estate he received was called Home Bush. Wentworth's son, William, was a president of the Sydney Turf Club, and in 1840, built a race track on the estate. This track was used as headquarters by the Australian Jockey Club, and so the first sport ever played on the Olympic Stadium site was a far cry from those that will be played there in the coming decades. Nonetheless, we can probably remain confident that the patrons of the venue in its early history were no less enthusiastic about their sporting interest than their ancestors will be in September 2000 and beyond.

In 1907, the State government resumed around 367 hectares of the estate, which had been increased in size since the time of the original grant to Wentworth, to establish an abattoir. History records show that the developers of this facility were less fortunate than us in their efforts, with the project running massively over budget. In 1968 stock sale yards were established on the land where Stadium Australia now stands. These were closed in 1990.

It was not until the 1980s that the Homebush Bay site began to take on its current character and complexion. The State Sports Centre, the Australia Centre and the

Bicentennial Park were constructed and opened prior to the 1988 Australian Bicentenary celebrations. At this point it is interesting to consider what might have happened had Sydney not won its bid to stage the 2000 Olympics. There is no doubt that Sydney's winning the right to host the Games of the 27th Olympiad was the key factor in the Homebush Bay precinct being what it is today—a first-class collection of sports facilities the equal of any in the world.

The Olympic Stadium that Sydney has acquired evolved from a dream by Multiplex and Hambros Australia. The bid teams from these organisations were led by Andrew Roberts and Alan O'Sullivan respectively. In October 1994, Australia Stadium 2000 consortium, the corporate embryo of what is now Stadium Australia Group, was one of seven which lodged expressions of interest in building and owning Sydney's Olympic Stadium. The consortium was expanded to comprise Multiplex, Hambros, Ogden International Facilities Corporation, Obayashi Corporation, Gardner Merchant (now Sodexho), Coca Cola Amatil, Tooheys, Ticketek, and Macquarie Bank, and the members were collectively committed to contribute around $40 million in equity to the project in the event their bid met success.

The Australia Stadium 2000 proposal involved building a stadium of 110 000 seats, compared with the bid requirement of 80 000. The extras were necessary to ensure that the membership scheme (described earlier) that was the core to our financial plan could guarantee members a seat at every Stadium event at the 2000 Games. A total of $364 million was to be raised by the membership scheme.

In March 1995 our consortium was one of three chosen to bid for the final Stadium contract, and on 11 September of that year, our bid was delivered to the OCA, as were those of our competitors. It is a project legend that one of the competitors delivered their documents in a finely crafted piece of timber cabinetry, while ours arrived in cardboard cartons after having being dropped on the footpath in the rush to meet the delivery deadline. Another case of content prevailing over presentation, those involved from our team at the time like to think.

On 23 January 1996 the OCA advised that Australia Stadium 2000 was the preferred bidder for the Stadium contract, beginning a long period of detailed negotiation which culminated with the signing of the project agreements on 9 September 1996. There were over 100 formal documents involved in the deal, and some 30 of these were regarded as 'material' agreements. The key document was the Project Agreement which confers on the Stadium Australia Trust, managed by MTM, the right to design, finance and construct the Stadium, and the responsibility to manage, maintain, and operate it until 2031, when it is taken over by the government. Other major agreements transfer elements of the Project Agreement defined responsbilities from the Trust to other parties. For example, design and construction responsibility is passed to Obayashi and Multiplex, and management and operations becomes the task of SAM and Ogden. Notwithstanding this, MTM, on behalf of the SAT, remains directly responsibility to the OCA for all Project Agreement responsbilities until handover in 2031.

Construction commenced on site on 10 September 1996.

Characteristics of an iceberg

Each of the two main roof arches are supported at either end by a thrust block. These are dwarfed by the temporary end stands until after the 2000 Olympic Games when the temporary end stands will be demolished. When this is completed, the thrust blocks will stand out as a strikingly attractive feature of the Stadium's design.

The thrust blocks have some of the characteristics of an iceberg. There is a lot more below the surface than that which appears above.

With the piers completed and a working base concrete slab in position, steel fixers begin positioning the heavy steel bars of the thrust block superstructure reinforcing system.

Right The reinforcement to the main base of a thrust block is completed. Note how the pier reinforcing steel extends upwards from the main base, hinting at the shape to come.

Left With formwork in position, the concrete to the first stage of the superstructure of the thrust block is pumped in. Note the progress on the main structural cores of the grandstand in the background at left.

Right The lower thrust block superstructure takes form. During the cool winter nights that occurred throughout the concrete curing process, the use of foil prevented heat loss.

A Widelux camera shot of the site in May 1997 gives an idea of overall progress, with the thrust block construction nearing the point of installation of the 6-tonne steel connection for the roof truss.

Ran McGregor and Jim Keaveney give a sense of scale to a completed thrust block. The pattern of smooth lines and scabbled concrete on the surface highlights the pleasingly aesthetic lines of this part of the structure.

Construction begins

A site overview in April 1997 shows bulk earthworks completed, the footing for the south-western thrust block well advanced (at bottom left), and piling to the eastern grandstand in progress (at right rear).

An overview of the site taken around January 1997. In the foreground, reinforcement protrudes from piling.

The site is a hive of activity in May 1997 as workers and machinery labour to complete the finishing touches to the footings of the western grandstand core. A concrete pump and boom (yellow) delivers concrete to a footing, while a piling rig (black) operates in the background.

It is May 1997 and the early morning sun emphasises the dominance of the core structure to the western grandstand over a site dotted with cranes and other machinery working among the maze of reinforcement protruding from pile footings.

A large steel reinforcement cage for a concrete column frames Barry Dobie of the crane crew who is directing the positioning of a load by two-way radio.

The truckloads of concrete used to construct the Stadium, if joined end to end, would stretch from Sydney to Newcastle. The destination was the hopper of a concrete pump, a most efficient method of spreading concrete around large area sites.

The booms of two concrete pumps busy with the pouring of a thrust block for a roof arch make an interesting pattern against the sky. The white building in the background is the Sydney Aquatic Centre, another Olympic venue.

The bright red boom of a concrete pump clearly frames the core structure of the eastern grandstand. In the foreground is the circular core of the northeastern access ramp. The ramp cores house rubbish removal chutes and important parts of the passive ventilation system.

Left and below Steel fixers complete the heavy steel reinforcement to the main core footing to the eastern grandstand. I often see art in the tough construction environment and this reinforcement cage was one of many sculpture pieces seen during the construction of Stadium Australia.

Right Workers construct the final areas of seating plats to the lower bowl in October 1998. A block wall to one of the arena entrances is being completed in the background.

This photograph was taken from the top of the south-western thrust block on a stormy afternoon and clearly shows the progress of the western stand as at June 1997.

The white steelwork is the floor structure of the corporate suites, which are cantilevered some 18 metres from the main structure. The brown steel columns supporting the white steelwork were removed several months later when the structure was completed.

Concrete is being pumped to the level 5 floor slab and the core structure is nearing completion.

It is July 1997 and the structure of the western stand is really taking shape as the roof arches are fabricated in the arena area.

The heavy, grey steel is the main structure supporting the cantilevered corporate suites. Note the different configurations for these grey frames: in the final product most are of the 'double diagonal' member type. The ones with no second major (lower) diagonal brace were a last-minute design change to allow even more flexibility to an already flexible suite layout design.

The four white steel members at the top of the picture were the first components of the upper seating tier structure to be installed.

Left A welder at work on the reinforcement 'cage' for one of the giant pile footings of the project.

Right Interesting patterns, with contrast enhanced by the strong mid-morning sun, formed by the scaffolding set up against the northeastern external wall of the building. It was most interesting to see the Stadium in various stages of development under different lighting conditions, particularly in the days of erection of the roof arches.

Workers make final adjustments to the reinforcement to the northwestern thrust block piles prior to pouring concrete.

The tight construction program necessitated much after-hours work on the project. In this shot, the northern stand framework is illuminated by the lighting used by a crew working on the fabrication of a roof-frame segment.

The Widelux camera emphasises the drama of the giant roof
arches contrasted high above the main concrete structure,
and against a dramatic cloud formation. Looking for glimpses
of art amid the frenetic site activity was a memorable stress-
control exercise.

A symphony in steel. The megashores supporting the western roof arches form a strong frame for the delicate-looking arch of the eastern roof structure. Below this the steel support framework for the precast seating plats to the upper level of the eastern grandstand can be seen taking shape. As always the giant Lampson crane commands centre arena.

Left With the structure well advanced, attention is turned to the arena preparation work. At the end of the arena closer to the camera, a giant sedimentation pit is under construction. This was useful in draining the arena during periods of heavy rain that threatened achievement of the construction program for the arena works. In the foreground, a worker takes a lunchtime nap on the sun-warmed steel plats of the northern grandstand seating.

The glazing to the level 3 east-side corporate suites can be seen taking shape in this picture. The 'inlets' in the glazing allow a wheelchair to move safely in the seating area. Each standard corporate suites houses 20 people and has 20 seats outside. One of these seats is separate from the others and can be quickly and easily removed to provide an external wheelchair position.

Much consideration was given to use of the Stadium by people with a disability. For example, to assist the vision impaired, all steps are marked in yellow, and there are tactile tiles placed at the top of each set of stairs. To assist the hearing impaired, there is an FM broadcast facility within the Stadium with hearing pieces provided on request. Special phones for the hearing impaired have also been provided. Each level of the building has special provision for wheelchairs and the access ramps each have a separate wheelchair 'lane'.

Left It wasn't all stress and pressure on site. Here a group of formworkers pose for a photographic recording of their contribution to the Olympic Stadium project. Pride of involvement was always evident among the people who worked on the project.

Right The completed seating plats in the lower bowl between the areas where the construction workers are busy are made of suspended post-tensioned in-situ concrete. It is this area of the seating that will move on rails to allow both rectangular field sports and AFL to be played at Stadium Australia after the 2000 Olympic Games and the Paralympics. More concrete seating plats were later constructed on the sloping earth area in front of the plats shown. These will be demolished after the Games and replaced by a metal-framed arrangement that will support nine rows of seating for rectangular field events and be tucked back under the concrete structure for AFL events.

A close look at this photograph reveals one of the main reasons that Obayashi, Multiplex and their sub-contractors were able to successfully complete the project in such a tight construction period. The footings to the core of the circular access ramp to the south-east corner of the Stadium are completed and the protruding commencement reinforcement to the walls is seen in the foreground. Above this, workers are busy constructing the formwork to the level 1 concrete floor slab. To the left, a team works on the concrete block retaining wall adjacent to the access ramp. Machinery can be seen in action in a number of locations. At the top left and centre of the picture, the southern end thrust blocks are well advanced.

Working on as many areas as possible simultaneously was one of the contractors' secrets of success.

Who called them *temporary* end stands? The structural core elements at the centre of this picture are part of the structure for the southern stand. The original concept of these end stands was for a lighter type of construction but the design development process proved the need for what was finally constructed.

The concrete structural core elements in this picture house the access stairs. The final incline of the upper seating tier is clearly indicated by the sloping side walls to each core element.

The first element of the roof sheeting can be seen top right. The sheeting is a cellular polycarbonate construction. The sheeting is light, flexible, sound and heat insulating and light transmitting. The areas of sheeting towards the front of the roof transmit some 48 per cent of incident light, providing for a softer contrast between areas of shadow and light in the arena. This aids in the clarity of TV images as it reduces the viewing impact when athletes move from lit to shaded areas and vice versa.

Further roof panels are being constructed in the arena area, some up to 80 metres long and weighing 140 tonnes.

Right This picture tells a couple of stories. The dark uprights at the right of the photo are temporary columns supporting the cantilevered corporate suites. These were removed when the structure was completed, leaving the suites suspended with their occupants, who provide a significant portion of the Stadium's revenue, closer to the action and experiencing the atmosphere from a better position than is achieved at any other similar Stadium in the world.

The keen observer will note a series of twin lines across the concrete slab from where the picture was taken. These are set-downs in the slab that have been filled with lightweight concrete for the period prior to the 2000 Olympic Games. After the Games, these set-downs will house the railway-type tracks on which sections of the lower-seating tier will move forwards and backwards to configure the Stadium for close audience proximity to both rectangular and oval field events.

Left Much of the concrete poured on the site was pumped into position. This picture shows workers positioning the concrete delivery hose for one of the final concrete pours to the lower seating bowl.

Left When the massive arched roof trusses are in position, it is difficult to appreciate their size. This photograph of Abdul Basal (lower) and Mick Lochmann, from National Engineering based in Young, New South Wales, working on a complex joint in the truss adds a human scale and gives some appreciation of just how big these structural members really are. Their length, 296 metres, approximates the distance between the try lines of three rugby fields (end to end). Their height, 14 metres, is about three times that of a single-level house.

The fact that these huge trusses were fabricated on the ground and positioned to very tight tolerances is a credit to Australian technology and the skill of our construction industry workforce.

The main roof arch trusses are supported at each end by high-density steel pins which allow rotation of the structure as it expands and contracts under initial loading and with changes in temperature.

Construction Manager, Ed Obiala, seen here with one of the 1.8-tonne pins, said he considered them a risk factor at one point of the project. While the cost of the pins was only in the order of tens of thousands of dollars each, if one had been damaged prior to erection, the time delay in having a replacement manufactured and transported from Germany could have cost hundreds of thousands, and perhaps even millions, of dollars.

Left The world's largest mobile crane was used for construction of much of Stadium Australia's roof. The crane was positioned in the centre arena and was moved along pathways of heavy timbers, seen clearly in this picture. The tracks of the crane are the height of an average sized person. The block-like component of the crane at right is the counterweight.

The crane, known affectionately as FBC (BC for 'big crane', not sure about the F), weighed 2600 tonnes and can lift a maximum of approx. 2000 tonnes. The most the device has ever lifted was reported to be 1500 tonnes; its heaviest job on Stadium Australia was lifting roof arch sections weighing around 250 tonnes.

Above This photograph shows the heavy timber track that had to be set up to move the world's largest mobile crane within the arena area. The timber spreads the load of the crane's weight and prevents bogging and damage to the drainage system beneath the arena surface.

On-site

Left A young workman inspects a column reinforcement prior to a concrete pour.

Right Serious discussions are in progress. MTM Stadium Management Limited Chairman, Stephen Rix (left), with new CEO of MTM Funds Management Limited, Andrew Bennett (seated), and Multiplex Directors Matthew Stagg and John Corcoran. John was previously a board member of Tower Hill Investments Managers Limited, before the name change to MTM Stadium Management Limited. Hambros and Multiplex originally each half-owned the Stadium Australia Trust Manager, Tower Hill. Societe Generale secured the Hambros holding after a buyout of the British-based parent company. In turn, MTM Funds Management Limited purchased 100 per cent of the shares of Tower Hill. MTM Funds Management Limited is owned by Multiplex, PBL (a Packer entity) and interests of Neville Miles and Simon Tripp.

News of the Packer interest received inordinate press at the time of the change in ownership, probably due to a lack of understanding that shareholding in the Trust Manager is quite a separate matter from shareholding in the ownership of the Stadium.

Left A workman checks the reinforcement for one of the main structural columns in the western grandstand.

Right Andrew Roberts of Multiplex 'walks the plank' across a section of muddy site with a couple of colleagues during a visit to the site by the project funding underwriters. Ralph Doubell, who wrote a foreword to this book, was one of the most fleet-footed of Australia's middle-distance runners, and an Olympic gold medallist at Mexico in 1968. On this particular day he was less fortunate than his friends in this picture, and learned from first-hand experience that even the fleet of foot have difficulty being nimble when one leg is buried nearly to the knee is mud. And he had a board meeting soon after the site visit. This day was definitely not one for the wearing of suits on-site!

This surveyor would be in the running for any innovative hard-hat design. With the precision of construction required these days, the surveyor is an essential, if often under-recognised, member of any project team.

Above Strength of character and a great deal of pride show on the face of this workman who was working on a 6-tonne thrust block connection piece for a roof arch when this photo was taken.

Right Chris Chapman of Stadium Australia Management Limited, checks the first turf laid at Stadium Australia, with Brian Thorburn of the Australian Rugby Union.

Lawrie Nethery was Multiplex's Construction Manager for the arena works. He was justifiably proud of the work on the track in particular. The design tolerances for the 100-metre track were 100 metres plus up to 30 millimetres, minus nothing. Stadium Australia's track was confirmed within these tolerances on its first check measuring. Congratulations Lawrie and the 'Mondo' track sub-contractor for a first-rate job.

The Multiplex senior management team for the project during a site visit. Ron Kofoed (left), Multiplex Director in charge of the project, Ed Obiala (in business as usual mode on the mobile) and Ross McDiven (right), Managing Director, with Chairman John Roberts AO. Ron Kofoed and I worked very closely on this project. I consider him, a fellow ex-Queenslander, to be an outstanding construction professional, demonstrating an exemplary level of client support and cooperation throughout the project.

Ron was away the evening we received the certificate of practical completion. Ross McDiven stepped into his shoes for that historic occasion.

Peter Luck signs off on an episode of Channel 7's 'Today Tonight' on the occasion of the first of the arena lighting being switched on. The date is 15 September 1998—two years from the opening event of the 2000 Olympic Games.

Sandie Watson, one of OCA's very capable media liaison people, made sure she got some OCA hard-hats on screen before her wave to the camera.

OCA Director of Stadia, Paul Gilbertson, (left) expresses satisfaction with progress on-site while Michael 'Greals' Grealy has a smile appropriate for the role of the OCA Director of Media Relations.

Chairman of Stadium Australia Management Limited, Paul
Isherwood, still manages a smile despite a miserable day on-site.

Underwriters to the Stadium Australia float reflect on the project's
financial history. OCA representatives joined us for the tour.

I have forgotten who pushed the camera button for this photograph of myself (left) and Chris Chapman during one of our many discussion tours of the quickly developing project. Stadium Australia Group consists of two entities: the owning Trust (of which I was the CEO of the trust management company) was responsible primarily for financing, design and construction issues. Stadium Australia Management Limited, run by CEO Chris Chapman, is responsible primarily for operation, maintenance and management of the facility. Without rapport between the management of these organisations, the project could have been a disaster. We didn't always agree with each other, but Chris and I emerged as great friends with a high respect for each other's very different management styles and personalities. We each had the knack of being a support for the other whenever corporate politics and pressure made life difficult.

Above Chris Chapman faces the media during one of the many announcements made about the Stadium. His years with Channel 7 were no doubt invaluable experience for his Stadium Australia role. At right is Bob Leece, deputy director of the OCA.

Right David Ghannoum and John Scicluna of Multiplex during one of many site inspections.

David's efforts, in particular, were instrumental in getting the site prepared for the first event. There were only 66 hours (to convert from construction site to operational Stadium) between Practical Completion and the first Rugby League match of the NRL Double-Header. David's job wasn't made easier by his wife, Clarissa, expecting (and overdue with) their second child. Ruben did the right thing by the project, waiting until 13 March 1999 to enter planet Earth. Unlike Stadium Australia, which was completed on time, Ruben was seven days late.

Steve Rixon, two-way radio in hand, worked with the Quality Rigging Services (QRS) crane crews on-site.

Eric Rolls and Ed Obiala of Multiplex manage a warm smile on a cool morning. Eric had a fantastic results-oriented attitude and was a great bonus to the project during construction.

Gary Galagher was one of the 'Manitowoc' crane drivers on-site.

Now here's a team that means business: one of the QRS crane crews who worked on the eastern grandstand.

At rear are (from left), Rod Saunders (QRS), Craig Goode (QRS), Ben Richens (MPX Crane Coordinator), and Dave Baker (QRS). Steve Rixon (QRS) is kneeling in front at right with another QRS employee who I was unable to identify.

Greg Le Quesne of Multiplex seems happy with progress on the laying of the arena turf base.

Right A smiling Chris Chapman takes his hat off to the work done by the world's largest mobile crane. Like most visitors to the site, Chris, a lawyer with the 'believe it when I see it' attitude of the survivor, was in awe of the huge dimensions of the crane.

Bill Buckland, as Design Manager, must have had one of the most important and stressful jobs on the Multiplex team, yet he always came up smiling. An engineer by profession, Bill spent several years in the USA satisfying his thirst for knowledge on structural design for earthquake-exposed regions.

I share with him an interest in religious and cultural philosophies from different countries of the world—a common interest that helped us get beyond many points of difference and arguments during the project. We've both learned to take our jobs, but not ourselves, seriously.

Above Despite the fact that their job looks, to the layperson, a little like separating the ends of a swimming-pool sized bowl of spaghetti, the boys from Team Commstar look happy with progress just days prior to completion.

Right Angela and her workmates from Sebel, who supplied the arena seating, take a break from their jobs — one of the most important on the project from an operational viewpoint — adding the seat numbers and row and aisle numbers right throughout the Stadium. The job of numbering some 110 000 seats took about six weeks.

Dave Baker, resplendent on-site in matching hard-hat and safety vest. Safety was always a key focus for all workers and visitors on-site, throughout the construction period.

Barry Dobie (Bazza) of QRS must have been a contender for the best decorated hard-hat vote, but the Multiplex boys probably would have preferred not to see their competitor's name emblazoned across the front. Barry worked with the QRS crane crews.

A focused workman takes a brief spell from fixing the reinforcing steel to the structure in the north-east quadrant of the building.

Mario Barrios brought the experience of being a member of the FUTSAL soccer team to the Multiplex side for the social match to test the Stadium facilities.

I was fascinated to talk with Uraguayan-born Mario about his background, and I know he had a great impact on my teenage son who was interested to hear the difference between Mario's childhood in Uraguay and the average Australian kid's childhood.

Mario initiated a charity drive among the sub-contractors and workers on-site which raised $60 000 for the Illizarov Clinic at the New Children's Hospital at Westmead.

Mario was a union representative on the project.

The athletes' tunnel

No detail has been overlooked in affording athletes the best possible chance of performing with excellence, for the 2000 Olympic Games in particular.

Track and field athletes will warm up and complete their final preparation at the Sydney International Athletics Centre (SIAC) track to the south-east of Stadium Australia. A tunnel has been constructed beneath the road that separates the two venues. This leads into the basement level of the Stadium where the dressing rooms are located. There are also four lanes of the same 'Mondo' material as the Stadium track, approx. 76 metres long, in the basement for those last practice starts etc.

Separating athletes from such distractions as the public and media is seen as important, particularly in the psychological preparation of elite athletes.

Above Waterproofing to the concrete roof of the tunnel is completed prior to the excavation being back-filled. The machine in the right foreground is compacting back-filled earth in layers to minimise movement and possible damage to any later work completed over the back-filled excavation.

Right Workmen place the steel reinforcement for the base and walls of the athletes' tunnel.

Fixing the roof arches

The erection of the massive arches that support Stadium Australia's roof is one of the truly inspirational stories in Australian construction history.

Each of the two main roof arches spans an amazing 296 metres. They are made up of hollow steel tubes, some up to a metre in diameter. Each arched truss weighs around 650 tonnes and, at its highest point, measures some 14 metres—that's about the same as three single-level suburban houses stacked on top of one another.

It is possible to construct these huge arched trusses in a number of ways: an intricate scaffold system, for example, could have been created together with some form of profile template, and the arch erected piece by piece in its final position. This, however, would have necessitated lengthy delays to the construction of some of the concrete elements of the building, notably the seating plats, and would probably have prevented the project being completed on schedule. After great deliberation, Multiplex and its designers and sub-

contractors decided that the main concrete structure and the roof arch construction must continue in parallel to comply with the schedule imperatives.

National Engineering won the contract to complete the work with Multiplex. They fabricated the steel components of the giant arched trusses in Young (in country New South Wales) and trucked them by semi-trailer the approximately 400 kilometres to the Stadium Australia site.

Here the arches were erected to profile on a template of columns set up in the area that would eventually become the main arena.

Craneage was of paramount importance because each arch was fabricated in three sections. The heaviest section weighed in the order of 250 tonnes—not a task for any standard construction crane. Multiplex hired a crane of impressive capacity; in fact, it was the largest mobile crane in the world. Originally constructed to lift rockets into their launch positions at Cape Carnaveral, USA, it was now located in Wollongong, lifting completed oil rigs from land to the water. This device weighed some 2600 tonnes and was capable of lifting a maximum of 2000 tonnes. Its work on Stadium Australia would be complex, but the weights to be lifted were well within its capability. On site, it became affectionately known as the FBC: the last two letters stood for 'big crane' but no one

would tell me what the F stood for—'fantastic', I guess.

The construction plan was to complete the thrust blocks, which would support the arched trusses at their ends. After this, the end sections of each truss would be lifted, then fixed into permanent position at the thrust block, and supported at the other end on huge, frame-like, load-bearing, steel-framed devices called 'Megashores'. The centrepiece of the trusses would then be lifted into position. However, this exercise was not as easy as the previous simple statement would suggest. The centre component of each arch was around 100-metres long, 14-metres high and it weighed in the order of 150 tonnes. The real challenge would be to lift this huge piece of steel structure into a gap equal to its own width plus the width of a weld (approximately 5–8 millimetres) either side.

The contractors' solution was to complete the task early on a winter's morning, where the cool ambient temperature would cause the steel in the arch structure to contract. The engineers' calculations indicated that the gap would increase to around 35 millimetres either side; hardly a comfortable working space, but a big improvement on the 5–8 millimetres originally available for the task.

Imagine the scene on-site as that first huge piece of steel structure was lifted into position. The 250-tonne,

100-metre long, southern-end section of the western grandstand roof arch was slung on the hook of the FBC a few days earlier in preparation for the lift into position. The deflection under its own weight was surveyed to ensure the 'fit' into its final position would work.

On the crisp and still morning of Thursday, 31 August 1997, consultants in suits and builders in stubbies gathered at dawn to witness a very special and very important piece of construction. The temperature was low and the excitement levels high and, to a person, hairs on the back of necks stood erect as, almost anti-climactically, the FBC hoisted the first arch section into position in a little less than 40 minutes.

A high-density, high-tensile steel pin, made in Germany and weighing 1.8 tonnes was positioned to secure the thrust block end and the 'free' end was bolted to flanges on the megashore.

For the rest of that day, you could literally feel the mood of achievement all over the site. Strangely, there was considerably less interest in the positioning of the remaining end sections—'been there, seen that' attitudes, I guess. However, all that was to change markedly on the morning of Saturday, 16 August 1997, when the centre section of the western arch was lifted into position.

Safe vantage points were in demand from the wee hours as people involved at all levels of the design and construction hierarchy sought the best position to witness Australian construction industry history in the making. All manner of video and photographic equipment was checked, loaded and re-checked in anticipation.

The onlookers were not to be disappointed. When all was ready, the FBC lifted 100 metres of steel—14-metres high and weighing 150 tonnes—into position above its final resting place. Without the use of the secondary craneage that had been positioned for the task, the driver of the FBC, a couple of metres off the arena floor, following instructions delivered by a team of six riggers, some 52 metres above, lowered the section into the gap with a tolerance space of 35 millimetres on either side, without incident. The tolerance for positioning at the temporary bolt positions was in the order of only 1.5 millimetres.

It is impossible to accurately describe the events of that morning in a way which records the emotion that prevailed. In 35 years in the construction industry I have never before seen anything so inspiring. People in suits joined in spontaneous discussion with people in construction garb in a way that does not often happen: the usual barriers broken by a common pride at being involved in this great project, the result of which will surely become an icon for Australia, and an important part of the country's sporting history.

The 'tall poppy syndrome'—the habit of criticising high achievers—is said to be thriving in Australia. That morning, we witnessed construction as good as it gets. We also witnessed the achievement of a mixed group of trades and professional people from many different ethnic backgrounds—all proudly Australian, all members of the Stadium Australia design and construction team, all bonded by pride of achievement—deliver a long-deserved and solid slap in the face to the tall poppy syndrome.

Innovative thinking and communication seldom gets as good anywhere in the world as it was on the Stadium Australia site that morning.

Right Fabrication of the centre sections of the trusses under way in the arena area. Note the steel-framed structure of the RAS pavilion buildings under construction in the background.

Left The end sections of the roof arches are seen under construction in the foreground with the centre sections progressing in the middle of the arena area. The white steel framework to the floor of the corporate suites has just been installed in the main structure shown at the top right of the picture.

Above Workmen look on as the first roof arch section is lifted into position on 31 July 1997.

Left Consultants, builders' staff and construction workers watch from every possible vantage point as the first arch truss section is lifted from its supports.

Left Workmen atop the
south-western thrust
block prepare to
connect the end of the
first roof arch sections.

Right The extension jib on
the world's largest mobile
crane is attached and the rig
for lifting roof sections can
be seen in perspective. The
tip of the crane would have
been over 150 metres above
ground level when this shot
was taken.

Left Dawn sunshine adds a golden glow as the centre truss section for the main western roof arch is hoisted from its arena template column supports.

Right In probably the most complex operation of the roof arches construction, a centre section is delicately lifted by the world's largest mobile crane into a gap its own length with only approximately 35 millimetres either side. The ropes hanging from the section were intended to assist in the final positioning.

Left After positioning of the centre truss section, welders waited for a daytime temperature of around 23 degrees centigrade for the steel to expand thereby closing the gaps between the sections in order for the welding of those joints to be completed.

The small roofed structures straddling the upper chord of the truss are the platforms from which the expert tradespeople completed this most crucial task.

Right This aerial shot shows the construction of the Stadium in full swing. Behind it is the Sydney International Athletic Centre which will be used as a warm-up facility by the athletes during the Games. To the left rear is the Sydney Aquatic Centre, venue for all Olympic pool events. To the right of the dual white buildings in the left foreground, Olympic Boulevarde, which leads to the Athletes Village, is under construction.

Left It fits!

Above The strong morning sunlight emphasises the beauty and drama of Stadium Australia's design well before its final completion. The centre truss section had been positioned just minutes before this photo was taken.

Right In the south-western corner of the building the first section of roof sheeting is in position. The concrete plats for the Gold and Platinum members' seating are nearing completion and the steel framing to the upper tier can be seen clearly at the top right of the picture.

Above My MTM colleague, Nicole Uren, is dwarfed by the giant roof arch during an inspection of the roof sheeting.

Rolling out the track

For several days in September and October 2000 the track at Stadium Australia will be the focus of world attention. Athletes at both the 2000 Olympic Games and the Paralympics will strive to cap years of dedicated, committed and sometimes tortuous and frustrating preparation with performance excellence. The Stadium Australia team wanted to make their own contribution towards giving these athletes the opportunity to achieve goals beyond their own wildest expectations.

The project team has striven to design and build a facility that is second to none in the world. The track received special attention, both from the project team and from the OCA, SOCOG and the various bodies involved with athletes at international level. The track and arena were prepared with a commitment to excellence. They are now ready to host world-standard performances.

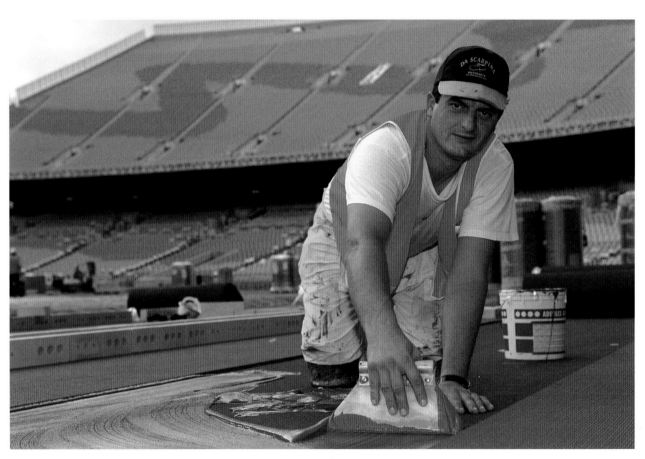

Left The 'Mondo' track material is supplied in strips 1.2 metres wide, and is simply rolled out over adhesive.

Above Vitoria Taschini was one of a team of four who travelled from Italy to lay the 'Mondo' running track. The team chose to continue its gruelling work despite 40 degrees centigrade temperatures above the bitumen sub-base in order to get home to families for Christmas. I saw these people as artists as much as tradespeople and it was a highlight of the project to see the skill and dexterity with which they spread the special adhesive, without wasting a drop, and cut the material to fit the track curves.

The joints in the track material must be perfect. After the track surface material is laid, concrete bricks are placed end to end over the joints. The adhesive is relatively quick drying and laying the track requires speed and agility in order to bring the used bricks from the back of the lines to the front where new track material has been freshly laid.

Laying the turf

The arena turfing system is high-tech in several components. Its overall design is by Multiplex's consultants, Ray Young and Associates, and involves a herring-bone patterned drainage system with layers of several different types of sand and gravel media. The arena surface is the 'StrathAyr' system, which consists of three components—loam, turf, and 'ReFlex' mesh elements. (ReFlex is a trademark.) The loam and mesh elements are mixed and laid over the prepared arena area to a depth of around 100–150 millimetres. The grass, with a cleanly washed root system, is rolled out over these materials.

The 'ReFlex' mesh elements, for which 'StrathAyr', an Australian company, holds global licences for sporting applications, serve a number of purposes. First, they provide a reinforced root zone which promotes vigorous turf development and growth. Second, they provide a degree of flexibility and resilience not yet proven, to the best of my knowledge, over any significant length of time by other turf systems (at least, not as of mid-1998 when I made the decision to use the system). This resilience affords some 'give' to players falling hard and so could contribute to fewer injuries. The resilience has also been shown to afford the opportunity for operators to place reasonably heavy weights on the surface with confidence that any indentations will quickly be gone soon after removal of the load. As the system compresses and flexes under load, it sucks air and nutrients into the root zone, thus promoting growth.

Joe McCullagh has been laying turf systems for many years. He was responsible for the Stadium Australia turf sub-base installation.

Right The loam and 'ReFlex' element mix of the arena turf sub-base is being laid. The hopper at rear is loaded from off-field with the pre-mixed loam and 'ReFlex' elements. It then feeds the distribution machine, compacting previously laid material as it does.

The thickness of the sub-layer can be clearly seen. Note the bitumen base to the 'Mondo' yellow-coloured 'D' zone at the end of the field area. The end of the pole vault run-up can be seen with the pole plant indent in place. The base for shot put/hammer throw can also be seen.

The project team

Over 1300 meetings of the contracting parties and their consultants and advisers were held during the design development phase, in addition to numerous others within the various consultancy groups. Designers made special explanation presentations of aspects of the project's design.

Discussion at these meetings was often vigorous, and meeting tables withstood the occasional thumping as points were emphatically made. This process of open discussion and creative/productive conflict contributed to the outstanding final product that Stadium Australia clearly is.

John Whatmore (left) and John Baker were key members of the Bligh Lobb Sports Architecture team on the project. They were from the Bligh Voller Nield side of the strategic alliance. Whatmore and Paul Henry (the latter from the Lobb side of the alliance) are two of the best presenters of architectural concepts I have known. Baker demonstrated commendable patience in attending hundreds of operator working sessions, and then adjusting numerous minor design details to make the Stadium a more effective venue.

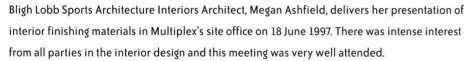

Bligh Lobb Sports Architecture Interiors Architect, Megan Ashfield, delivers her presentation of interior finishing materials in Multiplex's site office on 18 June 1997. There was intense interest from all parties in the interior design and this meeting was very well attended.

A body language expert would have a field day interpreting this picture: (from left) Tatsuya Myakawa of Obayashi Corporation, John Kleindienst and Alan Colegrave of Ogden International Facilities Corporation, and Paul Nikoten and Colin Ging of OCA show a similar intense interest, but differing reactions, to a design presentation. Bligh Lobb Sports Architecture's Megan Ashfield takes notes in the background.

Stadium Australia Management CEO, Chris Chapman, effectively turned his eye for detail to assessment of design presentations. Here, he takes the floor during a presentation by Paul Henry, a Director of Bligh Lobb Sports Architecture.

Richard Knight (left) of Ogden International Facilities Corporation and Raj Valluri of HOK Sport conduct a design review.

Chris Clarke of Bligh Lobb Sports Architecture looks intense during a design development meeting in Multiplex's site offices.

Right Nicole Uren, my right-hand (project manager) person, looking intense.

Centre right Bill Zagami, my college mate from Queensland Institute of Technology days in the late 1960s and early 1970s, and a colleague on a number of projects over the years, was one of our project management team for Stadium Australia. Here he looks perplexed at a point made during a design presentation.

Bill has a unique ability to lighten up any 'heavy' meeting with some (usually irreverent) smart crack at just the right moment. This quality was a great asset on the project.

Above Tatsuya Miyakawa of Obayashi Corporation personally checks the material proposed for the sun shades in the building.

Right Jeremy Pidcock was one of Multiplex's on-site quantity surveyors. The quantity surveyor is an essential member of any successful project management or site team.

James Sherriff was Multiplex's construction programmer. His job was to break the project down into manageable activities or tasks, to schedule these against a time line using advanced computer software, and to monitor subcontractor performance to ensure planned progress was being achieved. James also played goal keeper in the Multiplex soccer team, which christened the Stadium arena in a match to test the surface several weeks prior to practical completion.

Above left Above all, Stadium Australia's primary purpose is to be the stage for successful opening and closing ceremonies, soccer final, and track and field program for the 2000 Olympic Games. In this picture, SOCOG's Adrian Avis is looking vigilant, and perhaps a little doubtful, at a design meeting early in the project.

Above right John Kliendienst (JK) hangs on a point with interest. JK provided the operator's technical input during the design development process.

Alan MacTavish of Ogden International Facilities Corporation (left) reviews drawings with Colin Ging and Paul Nikotin of the OCA.

Above Bill Buckland, Multiplex's Design Manager, looking confident.

Left The writer (left) with MTMSM board members, Alan O'Sullivan, chairman Stephen Rix and Greg Paramor. (Photo by Karl Schwerdtreger)

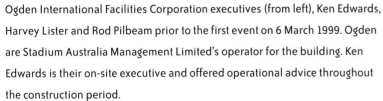

Ogden International Facilities Corporation executives (from left), Ken Edwards, Harvey Lister and Rod Pilbeam prior to the first event on 6 March 1999. Ogden are Stadium Australia Management Limited's operator for the building. Ken Edwards is their on-site executive and offered operational advice throughout the construction period.

Above John Corcoran, formerly of Hambros and now a director of Multiplex (left), and Andrew Roberts (right), were key Stadium Australia Group negotiators on the deal with OCA. With them is Peter O'Connell, a director of Stadium Australia Management Limited. Here they relax during the first event festivities.

Left Stadium Australia Management Limited Chairman, Paul Isherwood, is all smiles with the almost clockwork progress of the first event at the Stadium.

Jane Prisk, personal assistant to Chris Chapman, enjoys a peaceful moment in the newly completed venue.

David Cooksley is Multiplex's contracts administrator for the project. He's one of the best I've come across, with the expert negotiator's ability to look forlorn even if he were told he'd just won the lottery.

Multiplex efforts were led by director Ron Kofoed, one of many former Queenslanders (including myself) who worked on the project.

Multiplex's Michael Lonergan was project manager of the Sodexho catering equipment installation.

Left Dawn Carroll of Multiplex was responsible for the design and purchasing of several million dollars worth of furniture, fittings and equipment. She worked with Nicole Uren of MTM and Alan MacTavish of Ogden—they did a great job.

Below Martin Dymtruk of MTM looks proud to be involved.

Paul Nikotin of OCA (left), Adrian Avis of SOCOG, and Colin Ging of OCA using special Bose equipment that demonstrates exactly the sound from the public address system during the design phase.

I found this facility most helpful in making one difficult decision regarding sound to the temporary end stands. The equipment can reproduce the sound that would be experienced at any point in the Stadium the listener nominates. Multiplex Design Manager, Bill Buckland, and MTM Project Manager, Bill Zagami, observe proceedings at left of photograph.

Ulrika Fernstrom from Sweden was Multiplex's environmental engineer on the project.

One of the environmental measures taken during construction was to collect rainwater from the site and use it to prevent dust pollution which would otherwise have been caused by construction vehicles moving around the site.

Construction progress

The seating colour scheme was a matter of intense interest for all involved. Multiplex's architects presented five schemes from which we selected two for final consideration. At first, I was not convinced that the scheme we went with was the best, but my final decision was made in line with the opinions of others better qualified in matters aesthetic than yours truly. I particularly respected the opinion of Rod Sheard, a colleague from student days at the Queensland Institute of Technology, and Chairman of the Lobb side of Bligh Lobb Sports Architecture, Multiplex's architect on the project. After listening to Rod's advice, I spent hours agonising over the seat colour decision with Chris Chapman. Our main concern was that the seat colours would really define much of the character of the finished Stadium, and there would be no second chances to get it right.

The chosen scheme receives praise from virtually all who see it. It complements the curvo-linear aspects of the Stadium's design, and somehow is synergistic with Australia's blue skies and coastal environment. (I have found no concrete evidence in support of the popular modern legend that it was inspired by the design of a neck tie worn by a fellow drinker in a bar attended by our architect friends!)

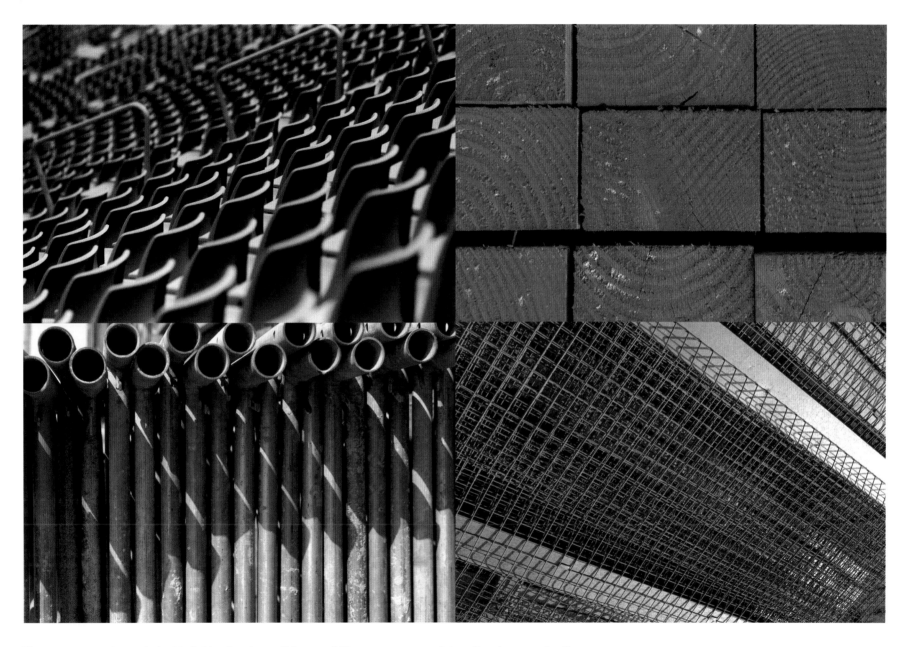

The construction site equivalent to 'taking time to smell the roses'. There are numerous interesting shapes and patterns on every site. Recording them on film makes for a pleasing diversion from the noise and pressure of the site environment.

A site tour group adds a splash of colour to the grey concrete interior before finishes were installed. The escalator void in the photographs serves a number of purposes: it is an impressive feature of the design and adds drama to the corporate and membership entry areas; it houses the escalators by which corporate patrons and members access their areas; and it acts as an entry and distribution shaft for natural light into the Stadium. To assist with this latter purpose, most of the walls around the void in the finished product are of glass bricks.

Previous pages Seating and aisles to the upper tier of a temporary end stand creates a striking pattern. The two-toned seating in the end stands is in the design of the logo used during the period in which Sydney was bidding for the Games. The picture at right shows a section of end-stand seating filled to capacity during the first event held at the Stadium.

The impressive dimensions and dramatic feel of the escalator void through each grandstand are evident in this picture. The opening at the top is under the upper seating tier and so allows light entry while being protected from the weather. The escalators that were installed in this void primarily serve membership and corporate areas. The light shaft aspects of the void contribute to reduced power consumption during daylight use of the Stadium.

Left The framework to hold the banquet hall sun shades takes shape. The built-in catwalks to facilitate cleaning of the external glazing of the building. Status of installation for the upper tier seating plats can be seen at the top of the picture.

Right This simple composition of shape, size and colour contrasts caught my eye during a site inspection late one afternoon. The steel structure to the upper seating tier is well advanced and the perimeter support structure to the roof is also progressing.

On a clear day you can see the geographic relationship between the Stadium and the City of Sydney. Parts of the Parramatta River, which links the two, can be seen at the top of the photograph.

This picture also shows the close proximity of Stadium Australia to other Olympic venues in the Homebush Bay precinct, which boasts probably the best collection of first-class sporting venues in the world. The Stadium is undoubtedly the jewel in the glittering crown. The Sydney International Athletics Centre (SIAC) track will be used as a warm-up facility for athletes and is linked to Stadium Australia by an underground tunnel. The track in Stadium Australia will be relocated at SIAC after the 2000 Olympic Games.

The white building to the right of the Stadium is the Aquatic Centre and will be used for the pool events of the Games.

Right A worker's safety gear adds a focal point to this photo taken simply for its artistic appeal.

Left Workers stand out against the grey seating plats of the western stand. The intense blue sky completes a simple but striking composition. Seeking such images was a pleasant distraction from everyday project management tasks with their attendant stress and frustrations.

Right Sun shade installation to one of the grandstands is about 50 per cent complete. The shades are of a perforated metal material, which allow building occupants to see out while blocking virtually all direct sunlight from entering the building. This adds to patron comfort and reduction in power consumption for air conditioning.

Left An interesting telephoto shot of the structural elements of one of the main stands.

Right This steel-framed tunnel eventually became the corporate suites, with the grey steel supporting structure housed in the partitions between the suites. Note that not all of the suites have the two diagonal braces, which affords flexibility in the configuration of the sizing of suites to meet market demands.

Left Looking a little like a 'sugar shaker', the north-eastern access ramp progresses in the warm morning glow. Construction to the neighbouring RAS facilities is under way in the background.

Right A close-up of the grid pattern formed by the roof sheeting installation also emphasises the pleasing curvo-linear shape of the roof on plan.

In these photos of the eastern (above) and western (right) stands, the towers on the far left and right are ready for fitting out with lighting and sound equipment, and the roof sheeting is advanced on both stands. The doorways at the bottom of the structure of the eastern stand will be extended through the yet-to-be-built remainder of the lower bowl and will provide access to the arena.

On the western stand, work to the lower bowl seating area can be seen progressing in the shadow cast by the roof structure. In the foreground are the steel seating plats of the upper tier of the temporary northern stand.

The telephoto lens picks out an interesting pattern within the supporting framework or the external sun shades.

Left The lower bowl seating viewed from directly above.

Left and opposite Reflections create an interesting picture of the Stadium under construction. A rainy day or two left water pooled in the set-downs in the concrete floor slabs in the northern stands. These set-downs would eventually house the floor finishes and some of the equipment supports to the floor of the food and beverage concessions.

It was a still day and the surface of the pooled water was like a mirror. To take the photograph I lay down partially in the water with the camera supported on a brick I put into the pool. After allowing the ripples to settle I was able to snap some interesting reflections. Even though it was a Sunday morning, there were a few workers on-site; some of their passing comments were, understandably, less than charitable.

The Great Stadium Walk

On 21 February 1999, the OCA staged a community inspection of Stadium Australia. Over 200 000 people expressed interest in attending The Great Stadium Walk, and 100 000 turned up on the day. The contracts in place did not anticipate such an event prior to completion of construction, and some debate was necessary before we could allow the event to proceed. The problem was resolved when a path was defined within the finished areas of the Stadium, and this area was cordoned off and controlled by the OCA. The visitors walked on the very track that will be the focus of worldwide attention during the track and field events of the 2000 Olympic Games and the Paralympics that follow. In addition to giving the community a chance to see Stadium Australia, the event afforded the opportunity for some of the Stadium Australia event day staff to don their new uniforms and test their skills in a 'live' Stadium environment.

Above Having passed the entry gates, these visitors look relaxed as they absorb the design features of the Stadium while strolling towards the entrance to the main arena.

Right Crowds queue in the precinct area between the railway station and the Stadium entrance soon after the gates were opened. The blue structures of the innovative precinct lighting towers can be seen in front of the Stadium. The wide-angle lens used for the shot has given the Stadium a compressed look somewhat reminiscent of the 'Ettamoggah Pub' of Australian cartoon fame.

Right This was the scene from level 4 of Stadium Australia as an enthusiastic crowd awaited 'doors open' for the community open day. Around 100 000 people took part in the day and their response was resoundingly positive.

Above The construction of the 'StrathAyr' arena turf system was a favourite point of interest.

Left Crowds stop in awe as they enter the arena area.

Right Three sides of the arena were crowded with people for most of the day, as this shot from the northern stand shows.

Visitors on-site

During construction, a long list of celebrities from the worlds of sports, media and politics visited the site. In the early stages these on-site visits created a lot of interest among the workers from all fields. After a while it all became a bit routine; however, interest in getting a picture with, or an autograph from, the sporting elite never faded as an extra-curricula site activity.

Right Two easily recognised sporting characters during a tour of the site were former Australian opening batsman David Hookes, now a Melbourne 3AW radio program host (with Gerard Healy of Australian Football fame) and Aussie Rules' Dermott Brereton (also now a Melbourne radio and television personality).

Right Host of 'The Games' (Channel 7 version), Tracy Holmes is an avid fan of the Stadium. Here she relaxes between shoots for the show that went to air on 21 February 1999.

I was privileged to escort British Opposition Leader, William Hague, on a private tour of the site one Sunday morning in March 1998. In this photo he expresses intrigue at the size of the structures supporting the temporary grand stands. With him is Multiplex's Ed Obiala.

AFL chief, Wayne Jackson, faces the media throng on the announcement that AFL would be played at Stadium Australia. With him are New South Wales Premier, Bob Carr, and CEO of Stadium Australia Management Limited, Chris Chapman (blue shirt, striped tie).

Melinda Gainsford-Taylor poses with a group of construction workers during one of her visits. The guys were on their way home, but had their hard-hats ready for the autograph ritual. Melinda was a favourite with all on-site, always willing to provide a signature and always with a smile. (Photo by Nicole Uren.)

Cathy Freeman during a visit to the Stadium just before its completion. Cathy says she runs just because she loves running. I consider her one of the most down-to-earth, committed and inspirational people I have ever met.

Sebastian Coe, OBE, former British Olympian and, until recently, 800-metre (athletics) world-record holder, visited the site on two occasions. His first inspection was squeezed into a few spare hours between a speaking engagement and a flight back home. His second was when he accompanied British Opposition Leader, William Hague, on a tour. 'Seb' has followed a career in politics since his days on the track; a former member of the British Parliament, he is now Private Secretary to William Hague.

In this picture, Ed Obiala, always an available, willing and capable celebrity tour guide, points out the structural features.

Right Two giants of the sporting world meet. CEO of the AFL, Wayne Jackson, has a few words with former Wallaby Captain and Stadium Australia Management Limited Board member, Mark Ella, on the occasion of the announcement that AFL would be played at Stadium Australia. Mark Ella represented Australia 25 times, taking part in eight tours between 1979 and 1984. He captained the team ten times.

Australian women's javelin champion and 1996 Olympian, Joanne Stone, adds her autograph to Ed Obiala's construction hat. Ed used a couple of hard-hats during the course of the project—not enough room for all signatures on one—and secured the autographs of some very interesting people from all over the globe. His insistence on personally approving every site visitor ensured he didn't miss any significant signatures.

Jon Konrads was just 14 years old when he won swimming gold at the 1956 Olympics. Here he autographs Ed Obiala's new hard-hat. Jon is still involved with swimming and, on the day this picture was taken, told of a swim training video he was about to release (intended for the general public rather than elite athletics).

Testing 1, 2, 3

When it was time to test the near-completed facilities, what better way than with a soccer match? Multiplex challenged concreting sub-contractors, De Martin and Gasparini.

The match was played in the early evening and allowed the opportunity to test the arena lighting, the recently laid turf, and the giant Panasonic video screens. All passed the test with flying colours.

De Martin and Gasparini won the match, balancing an earlier victory by Multiplex in a match played at an outside ground.

A De Martin and Gasparini player about to shoot for goal with Multiplex site personnel in hot pursuit.

Top left The Multiplex faces tell the story at half-time, and the video screen records it all in brilliant colour.

Bottom left It's dirty work but somebody has to do it. Two delighted spectators enjoy the match from the corporate suite, which served us well as an office during the latter months of construction. Eric Rolls of Multiplex and Bill Zagami of MTM Stadium Management Limited got a great view of the match and the screens and, of course, sorted out a few minor contractual issues in the process.

Far left Being first is important at Stadium Australia, and that includes being the first streakers.

Two construction workers, wearing their knickers around their knees and construction hard-hats for protection, streaked onto the field during the Multiplex versus De Martin and Gasparini match. When they spotted my camera pointed their way, they immediately turned around—out of modesty, no doubt. The small but enthusiastic crowd of onlookers roared their appreciation as the closed-circuit TV camera projected them full frontal and in glorious colour on the giant Panasonic video screens.

It was undies up for the long jog back across the field.

The first event

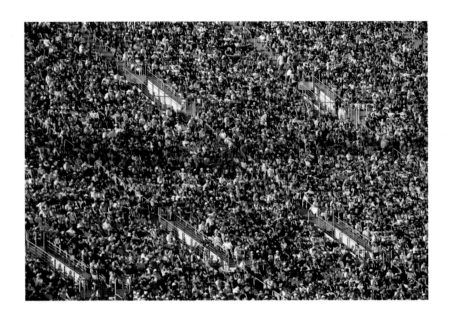

The end stand was filled to near
capacity well before the kick-off
to the main events.

Above Blanche Stack checks on the
final preparations in the Gold
Members' fine dining restaurant.

Right, top Customer Safety (security)
team personnel share a laugh
immediately prior to taking up their
posts for the big day.

Right, bottom Customer service
personnel in high spirits just before
their final briefing.

Above 1968 Olympic 800-metres gold medallist and Stadium Australia Management Limited Board member, Ralph Doubell (third row back, leaning forward), enjoying the evening from the owners' suite. OCA's Director of Stadia, Paul Gilbertson (second row, far left), is camera conscious as his wife, Dianne (seated next to him) discusses the on-field action. Perpetual Trustees representative, Ray Kellerman looks relaxed in the rear seating (blue check shirt).

Above Stadium announcer, Grant Goldman (left), and
Ogden's General Manager of Events, Richard Knight, complete
final tests on the public address system prior to the gates
opening.

Right Project Manager, Nicole Uren, who moved from Melbourne to
work on the project, inspects the field with just a few minutes to go to
'gates open'.

Far right The pre-match entertainment of the first event in full swing.

Appendix 1
In a nutshell

The Stadium provides for 110 000 seats during the Olympic Games, and will undergo major conversion work to provide approximately 80 000 seats after the Games. In its pre-Olympics configuration, the Stadium is used primarily for rectangular-pitch football codes. However, the structure has been enhanced to allow for playing Australian Rules after the Games. This will be achieved by construction of a system of moving seats within the lower bowl. Forty-seven rows of seats, around 95 metres long on either side of the arena, will move about 15 metres backwards and forwards on a rail system. These will be moved forward for rectangular field sports and back for Australian Rules matches.

The upper tier of the end stands will be removed after the Games and be replaced with a roof at each end.

PROJECT MILESTONES

Commencement on site	9 September 1996
Milestone No. 1 Completion of footings	19 March 1997
Milestone No. 2 Completion of erection of steel roof trusses	27 September 1997
Milestone No. 3 Energising of substations	4 April 1998
Milestone No. 4 Completion of pre-cast concrete seating plats to the upper tiers	13 June 1998
Practical Completion	1 March 1999

FACTS AND FIGURES ABOUT THE STADIUM

Building cost at completion	$650 million
Site area	16 hectares
Concrete used	90 000 cubic metres
Structural steel	12 000 tonnes
Reinforcing steel	10 000 tonnes
Total roof weight	4100 tonnes
Roof size	30 000 cubic metres
Biggest single crane lift	250 tonnes
Number of piles	2600
Main arch span	295.6 metres

STADIUM SEATING NUMBERS IN PAST OLYMPICS

1972	Munich	80 000
1976	Montreal	79 000
1980	Moscow	100 000
1984	Los Angeles	101 000
1988	Seoul	100 000
1992	Barcelona	60 000
1996	Atlanta	83 100
2000	Sydney	110 000

POINTS OF INTEREST

- The Stadium is the largest ever built for an Olympic Games.
- The arena will be the venue for the opening and closing ceremonies, all track and field events, the soccer final and the marathon finish.
- After the Olympics, the Stadium can be used for sporting events such as soccer, rugby union, rugby league and Australian Rules football as well as a range of concerts.
- Four Boeing 747s would fit side to side under the span of each main roof arch, which are each the length of Sydney's Glebe Island Bridge.
- The building consists of two main grandstands and two temporary end stands.
- The upper levels of the temporary stands at the north and south ends each hold approximately 14 000 spectators. After the Olympics and Paralympics are completed these stands will be removed and the lower bowl seating in this area will be covered with a polycarbonate roof.

- The crane that lifted the main arch into position is the largest mobile crane in Australia and one of the largest in the world.
- Up to 25 cranes with capacities ranging from 5–250 tonnes were used in the construction of the Stadium.
- The amount of excavation carried out is equivalent to the volume of around 1500 standard suburban homes.
- The footings for the stands and the thrust blocks (which support the weight of the roof arches) consist of concrete slabs up to 2.2 metres thick poured on top of 2600 piles.
- The 18 000 trucks that delivered the concrete required for the superstructure, parked end to end, would stretch from Homebush to Newcastle.
- The million masonry blocks used, if laid end to end, would stretch 400 kilometres.
- The paint used to finish the roof structure would be sufficient to paint 10 000 family sedans.
- The total length of the welding rods used in joining the roof structural steel would be enough to stretch across Australia, or wrap around New Zealand several times.
- If the urinals were joined end to end, there would be nearly enough to go around the external perimeter of the facility.
- There are 128 entrances to the seating bowl (formally described by the delightful word 'vomitories') in Olympic configuration.
- There will be around 90 tonnes of garbage generated by the average full-house event at the Stadium.
- There is sufficient carpet in the Stadium to cover the lounge rooms of 1000 average suburban homes.
- The steel members in the roof structure, if laid end to end, would extend more than six times the distance of Sydney's 'City to Surf' run.

- The arena seating, if stacked vertically, would reach skyward, through the stratosphere and over 20 kilometres into space.
- The tubing used to distribute beverages (and the gases used in their dispensing) throughout the Stadium is long enough to reach from Campbelltown to the Sydney Town Hall.
- When corporate box fit-out is completed, there will be 500 television sets in the Stadium.
- Each of the two giant Panasonic video screens is the size of 540 domestic 50cm television sets, or about the same size as the floor plan of the average suburban home.
- There are nearly 100 food and drink outlets in the Stadium. In addition there is a 2900 square-metre main kitchen and 18 satellite kitchens and serveries.
- There are over 18 000 steps in the Stadium. If you climbed every one, it would be the equivalent of reaching the summit height of Mt Kosciuzko.
- The Stadium can cater for around 5500 sit-down diners simultaneously—far more than any other stadium in the world.
- There are about 8500 square metres of turf in the arena pre-Olympics. After the Games, this will be increased to 19 000 square metres to allow Australian Rules football to be played.
- It takes 70 kegs of beer to fill the lines before a single drink can be poured in full house configuration. During a major event, over 1000 kegs of beer will be consumed.
- There are 180 kilometres of electrical cabling in the Stadium.

RESPECTING THE ENVIRONMENT

The design focus

- Passive ventilation, i.e. ventilation without any mechanical devices, has been integrated in the Stadium. Full air conditioning has been minimised to conserve energy.
- The need for artificial lighting has been reduced as the Stadium allows maximum intake of daylight through especially constructed light voids.
- Stormwater will be collected from the Stadium roof and stored in large tanks for irrigation of the pitch.
- The Stadium design has minimised the use of PVC and all building materials are subject to Life Cycle Assessments to determine their environmental impacts prior to any design decisions being made.
- Environmentally friendly gas fired co-generators reduce the demand of the Stadium on the main grid supply of electricity.

And during construction

- Waste separation was part of the Stadium construction process. Waste was separated into a number of streams with disposal for recycling where appropriate.
- Dust and air emissions were minimised by the watering of roads, provision of truck wheel-wash, provision of silt-fences and enforcing special requirements for plant maintenance.
- Stormwater was collected and diverted to a sedimentation pond on site for further transport and treatment in the Haslam Creek sedimentation place.
- Noise was regularly monitored to ensure emissions were kept within acceptable limits.

PREPARING FOR THE OLYMPICS AND PARALYMPICS

The completion of Stadium Australia was focused on producing a stadium that can be used with the utmost versatility. This approach has given the Stadium Australia Group the opportunity to stage a number of major sporting events during the eighteen months leading up to the Games. The early events were invaluable to us in detecting any 'bugs' in the Stadium and rectifying them well in advance of September 2000 when the Games begin.

Preparation for the Games commenced in August 1999, and work will continue right up until the days before the opening ceremony. Representatives of the OCA, SOCOG, Stadium Australia Group, and Multiplex negotiated a preparation program that will allow the staging of a full schedule of pre-Olympic football matches and other Stadium events. The program also ensures that there will be no delay to, or reduction in, the quality of the adjustments that must be made to the Stadium prior to the opening ceremony.

Following is a schedule of the major elements of work that will be completed between mid-August 1999 and 15 September 2000, when the Olympic Flame will be lit at Stadium Australia.

- Offices for SOCOG will be constructed and fitted out in the basement and on level 3 of the Stadium for use until after the Games.
- Structural changes will be made to elements of the Stadium to cater for the special requirements of the opening ceremony.
- A substantial number of seats will be removed from the southwest quadrant of the lower seating bowl, and be replaced by a 'tribune' from which the journalists of the world will watch events and begin to prepare their reports.
- Press boxes and coaches boxes presently located on level 2 of the western stand will be dismantled and removed.
- A 'venue press centre' will be constructed and fitted out in the southern end of the basement service level, under the southern grandstand.
- A media conference room will be constructed in the basement service level.
- A photographers' work area will be constructed in the basement service level.
- Adjustments, including the establishment of offices and medical rooms, will be made to the existing change rooms in the basement service level.
- Doping control facilities will be established in the basement service area.
- The entry for the opening ceremony's Parade of Nations will be prepared.
- The entry to the athletes/media mix area will be completed.
- The final call area for athletes will be fitted out.
- Medal ceremony staging will be constructed.
- An athletes' lounge will be fitted out.
- The television cable 'entry room', currently a bar concession on level 2, will be newly fitted out.

- Television cabling will be installed throughout the building.
- Bridging will be constructed between the international broadcasting centre next to the Stadium and the Stadium itself to carry the TV cabling.
- Offices will be constructed and fitted out on levels 4 and 5 of the Stadium.
- Television outside broadcast van locations will be established.
- Flags of all the nations competing in the Games will be erected in the Stadium.
- A 'VIP entry canopy' will be constructed at the entry to the western grandstand.
- Two major pieces of sculpture, prepared by New Zealand artist, Neil Dawson, will be erected, one above the main entries to each of the east and west grandstands.
- SOCOG will install drug-testing equipment in the doping control rooms.
- SOCOG will install its timing equipment.
- SOCOG will install its photo-finish equipment.
- SOCOG will install all furniture and fixtures to all the rooms established for the Olympic period.
- Telstra will complete installation of its equipment and the information technology fitout will also be completed.
- SOCOG's field equipment will be installed.
- The Olympic scoreboards will be installed.
- The cauldron for the Olympic flame will be installed.

POST-GAMES WORK ON STADIUM AUSTRALIA

After the closing event of the Paralympic Games, an army of workers will swing into action to reconfigure Stadium Australia from its Games format to that required for its 50-year design life. Well over $100 million will be expended on the conversion exercise.

MTM Stadium Management Limited, as manager of the Stadium Australia Trust, is responsible to the New South Wales government for these changes. Obayashi and Multiplex will carry out the works for the Trust.

The work that must be completed is substantially more than was expected at the commencement of the project. Since then, the decision has been taken to play Australian Rules (AFL) matches at Stadium Australia and this necessitates some $25 million extra design and construction work during the conversion period. The Stadium must be ready for AFL matches from March 2001 and in addition, must also be able to host major rugby league and rugby union matches through the 2001 season. This places stringent restraints on the construction program. All of the work must be completed by March 2002, so Multiplex and their subcontractors will be very busy indeed between the completion of the 2001 season and the commencement of the next.

Following is a schedule of the major things that will occur in the planned conversion:

- All SOCOG furniture, fittings and equipment will be removed.
- Temporary SOCOG offices etc. will be demolished.
- The Olympic track will be lifted and relaid to replace the SIAC warm-up track.
- The front ten rows of seating of the eastern and western grandstands (lower bowl) will be removed and their supporting structure demolished.
- The lower bowl seating in the four corners will be removed and the supporting structure demolished.
- The photographers moat will be removed.
- The lower bowl component of the end stands will be jacked up and moved forward some 15 metres.
- The arena grass and drainage system will be extended from the current approx. 8000 square metres to around 19 000 square metres to provide a field suitable for Australian Rules football.
- The upper level seating to the end stands will be removed and the supporting structure demolished.
- A roof will be constructed over the end stands, which will, by then, consist of lower bowl seating only. The end roofs will be of similar construction to the existing eastern and western grandstand roofs and will connect to them.
- Seating will be repositioned to 500 millimetre spacing from the existing 480 millimetre spacing (centre of seat to centre of seat). Ownership may reconsider this component of the conversion.
- Change rooms will be adjusted to suit all football codes including the AFL.
- Foundations will be prepared, tracks laid and 47 rows of lower bowl seating some 95 metres long in both the eastern and western grandstands will have wheels fitted to allow

movement forward and backwards. This will give patrons close proximity to the field of play for all football codes.

- A telescopic structure will be installed to house the seating to the front rows of the sections of the lower bowl that will be 'on wheels'. The telescopic seating will be withdrawn under the main seating structure when this is moved to its rear position for AFL games. The reason the telescopic seating is withdrawn is to 'fit' the stadium seating to the curved sideline of the AFL field.
- Bridges will be installed to allow patrons to pass from the concourses of the main stadium structure to the seating areas of the lower bowl when the movable seating is in the forward position.
- Food and drink concessions to the end stands will be repositioned to suit the newly configured concourse arrangement.
- Outbuildings constructed on the ground level beyond the main Stadium perimeter will be demolished. These outbuildings house toilets until after the Olympics and Paralympics.
- The television cabling that was installed for the Games will be removed and the 'cable entry room' will be re-established as the bar/food concession that it was pre-Games.
- One of the scoreboards will be removed.
- The external precinct surface will be rebuilt as necessary where the end stand conversion work took place.
- The press box will be reinstalled on level 2 of the western grandstand.
- All building services will be refitted and commissioned to suit the new configuration of the Stadium.

Appendix 2
Key parties

Owning trust: Stadium Australia Trust

Trustee	Perpetual Trustee Company
Trustee's representatives	Raymond Kellerman
	Jodie Boone

Trust manager/owner's representative: MTM Stadium Management Limited (formerly Tower Hill Investment Managers Limited)

Chairman	Stephen Rix
Board	Alan O'Sullivan
	Greg Paramor
	Neville Miles
	Simon Tripp
CEO and project director	Alan Patching
Project managers	Nicole Uren
	Bill Zagami
	Peter Bishop
	Gary Brown
Financial controller	Jim Harte
Company secretary	Grant Winberg
Personal assistant to Alan Patching	Maria Humphreys

Consultants to the Trustee

Guttridge, Haskins and Davey	Tom Pinzone
	David Hickie
	Rick Piliz
Davis Langdon and Beattie	Ian Jackson

Legal adviser to Stadium Australia Group
Freehill Hollingdale and Page
Tax adviser to the Stadium Australia Group
PricewaterhouseCoopers

Government authority: The Olympic Coordination Authority

Director of Stadia	Paul Gilbertson
Development adviser	Colin Ging
Development managers	Greg McTaggart
	Peter Lacy
	Paul Nikotin
	Warren Paris
	Bernard Connell
Development consultants	Mark Ingram
	Malcolm Alger
Site manager	Dennis Claxton
Executive assistants	Maria Cominos
	Allison Wright
Project assistant	Mark Lewis

Consultants/advisers to the Olympic Coordination Authority

Architectural adviser	HOK Sport
Structural and vibration	Taylor Thomson Whitting Pty Ltd
Acoustics	Peter R Knowland & Associates Pty Ltd
Lighting	George Floth Pty Ltd
Hydraulics	The LHO Group Pty Ltd
Building and mechanical services	George Floth Pty Ltd
Vertical transportation	Norman Disney & Young
Audio	Wrightson, Johnson, Haddon & Williams Inc.
Olympic plaza	Denton, Corker, Marshall Pty Ltd
Crowd modelling	Arup Transportation

Geotechnical	Jeffrey and Katauskas Pty Ltd
Vibration adviser	Richard Heggie and Associates Pty Ltd
Pylons architect	Tonkin Zulaikha Architects
Pylons structural	Taylor Thomson Whitting Pty Ltd
Pylons electrical	Barry Webb and Associates
Pylons signage	Emery Vincent Design Pty Ltd
Legal advice	Clayton Utz
Quantity surveying services (pylons)	Currie and Brown
Asset management advice	Advanced Asset Solutions

Operational management: Stadium Australia Management Limited

Chairman	Paul Isherwood (after resignation of Peter Ritchie)
Board	Ralph Doubell
	Greg Paramor
	John Curtis
	Mark Ella
	Michael Easson
	Peter O'Connell
CEO	Chris Chapman
Company secretary	Grant Winberg
Personal assistant to Chris Chapman	Jane Prisk

Financiers to Stadium Australia Group

ANZ Bank
ABN Amro

Underwriters to Stadium Australia Float

ANZ Bank
ABN Amro
Deutsche Morgan Grenfell
Macquarie Bank

Operator: Ogden International Facilities Corporation

Directors	Harvey Lister
	Ken Edwards
	Rod Pilbeam
Design and construction phase reps	John Kliendienst
	Richard Knight
	Darryl Kerry
	Anthony Duffy
	Anita Moreno
Personal assistant to Ken Edwards	Ilka Nadin

Caterer: Sodexho Australia

Managing director	Jonothan Knight
General manager	Richard Errington
Executive chef	Dieter Grun
Retail catering manager	John McHugh

Head contractor: Obayashi Corporation

Representatives	Mr Sano
	Mr T Seto
	Mr T.Miyakawa

Main contractor: Multiplex Constructions Pty Ltd

Director in charge	Ron Kofoed
Construction manager	Ed Obiala
Design manager	Bill Buckland
Engineering services design manager	Keith Parslow
Project site team	Mark Ainsworth
	Don Aroney
	Dawn Carroll
	David Cooksley
	Ulrika Fernström
	David Ghannoum
	Mark Hetmanski
	Jim Keaveney
	Greg Le Quesne
	Michael Lonergan
	Ranald McGregor
	Lawrie Nethery
	Jeremy Pidcock
	Eric Rolls
	Bruce Scotland
	James Sherriff

Appendix 3
Authorities and Multiplex's consultants

AUTHORITIES

Olympic Co-ordination Authority, Energy Australia, Telstra, Sydney Water, AGL Gas Company (NSW) Limited, Workcover Authorities, E.P.A. N.S.W., SOCOG, Department of Energy, NSW Fire Brigades, DUAP

CONSULTANTS

Flora/Fauna	Australian Museum Business Services
Architect (Sydney)	Bligh Lobb Sports Architecture
Passive Ventilation	Brian Ford & Assoc
Pitch & Arena Geotechnical	Coffey Partners International Pty Ltd
Traffic	Colston Budd Hunt & Twiney Pty Ltd
Corrosion	Corrosion & Coating Inspection Services
Graphic Design	Emery Vincent Design
Environmental	Enproc Pty Ltd
LCA	ERM Mitchell McCotter
I.T. Services	Flack & Kurtz Consulting Engineers
I.T. Services	Flack & Kurtz Australia Pty Ltd
Furniture, Fittings and Equipment	Forbes & Harris
Video	Hayson Promotions
Advice re access for people with disabilities	Independent Living Centre NSW Inc
Daylight Analysis	Insearch Limited (UTS)
Carpet	Jim Cooper & Assoc
Environmental monitoring	Johnstone Environmental Technology Pty Ltd
Environmental Advisor	Karla Bell & Assoc
Natural and Artificial Lighting	Lighting Design Partnership
Architect (London)	Lobb Partnership Ltd
Legal	Minter Ellison Lawyers
Structural Engineer	Modus Consulting Engineers in association with Sinlair Knight Merz Pty Ltd
Bird Proofing	M Way & Associates
Local Industry Participation	NSW ISO Ltd
Air Quality	Nigel Holmes & Assoc
FF&E (Technical)	RGC Consulting
Acoustic	Robert Fitzell Acoustics Pty Ltd
Electrical & Mechanical Engineer	D Rudd & Partners in association with Sinclair Knight Merz Pty Ltd
LCA	Scientific Certification Systems
Quality Assurance	SGS Certification Services
Hydraulics Engineer	Sinclair Knight Merz Pty Ltd
Landscape – Precinct	Site Image Landscape Architects
Fire Safety	Stephen Grubits & Associates
Lighting	Thorn Lighting Pty Ltd
Perspective	Tim Throsby & Assoc
Building Certifier	Trevor Howse & Assoc
Photovoltaics Analysis	Unisearch Ltd
Programme	Len Keeble
Wind Analysis	University of Sydney
Crowd Modelling	Veitch Lister Consulting Pty Ltd
Quantity Surveyor	W T Partnership
Return Facility Brief	Briggs Brindle
Asset Management	Domain Consulting
Lifecycle	Scientific Certification
Pitch and Arena Design	Young Consulting Engineers
Training Site Supervision	Osmo Consultants
Moving Stands(options)	VSL Prestressing / Herk Edwards
Training	Housing Industry Association
Planning Consultant	Ingham Planning
Food and Beverage	Mack Group
Surveyor	Frank Mason / Whelan's
Safety	Skillvance
Printer	DES Digital Copy Centre

Appendix 4
Multiplex's subcontractors

Earthworks .... Daracon Group

Tree Relocation .... Tree Doctor

Temporary Electrics .... Galpern Electrics

Structural

Steel to Arch, Roof, Mid & Upper Tiers .... National Engineering

Bored Piers .... Frankipile Australia

Reinforced Concrete Structure .... De Martin & Gasparini

Site Accommodation .... James Hardie Building System

Site Accommodation .... Campac

Facade Support Frame .... Solari Welding Contractors

Plan Printing .... Des Copying

Prestressing .... Vsl Prestressing

Temporary Electrics .... N&G Electrics

Temp/Permanent Hydraulics .... J R Keith

Security Services .... The Barrington Group

Cranage .... Lampson Cranes

Cleaning Services .... A Clean City

Pest Control .... Gold Shield Pest Management

Siphonic Drainage .... Armpower

Temporary Electrics Design .... Roles Electric

Temporary Fencing .... Colemans Fencing

Electrical .... Kennedy Taylor

Mechanical/ Fire Services/ Doors & Frames .... Tyco

Site Accommodation .... Eastern District Carpentry

Lifts .... Honeywell

Escalator .... Kone

Canteen .... Evedale

Videoboard .... Panasonic

Man/Materials Hoists .... Walco Hoist Rentals

Precast Seat Plats Upper Tier .... Rescrete

Bus Services .... Formquay Pty Ltd (Shire)

Level 6 Steelwork, Level 7-8 Steelwork, Ramp Cladding, Truss to N & S Stands .... Wollongong Fabrications

Blockwork .... Fugen Holdings

Temporary Covered Walkways .... Rocom

Concrete Cutting .... Hardcore

Concrete Cutting .... Ripa

Polycarbonate Roof .... Specialist Glazing Systems

Sub Station Fitout .... Energy Australia

North & South Stands Steel .... Transfield

Cement Render .... Lidcombe Plastering

Handrails/ Metal Work to Fire Stairs, Upper Tiers, Mid Tiers, Lower Tiers .... Icon

Pa System .... P A People

Television System .... Global

Tele-communication .... Commstar

Security System .... Honeywell

Core 4 Ramp Rooves .... Pacific Steel

Lighting Masts .... Future Engineering & Communications

Tree Supply .... Karignan Plantations

Facade Access .... Concept Hiring Services

Metal Facade Cladding .... Axis Building Group

Seating .... Sebel Furniture Ltd

Ceramic Tiling .... Deemah Marble & Granite

Joint Sealant/ Grouting .... Network Building Systems

Painting .... A & D Koureas

Drywalls (West Stand) .... Interfit Pty Ltd

Drywalls (East Stand) .... Interline Interiors

Substation Metalwork .... Aardvark Metal Fabrications

Core Drilling (Facade) .... Metro Core Pty Ltd

Shed Relocation .... Kanabrook Cranes Pty Ltd

Glazed Balustrades .... Yap Engineering

Track .... Mondo

Central Void Scaffold .... Boral Building Services

Paving Prototype .... J.A. Bradshaw

Internal Glazing .... Architectural Glass Projects

Specialist Ceilings .... R T & D J Fairbrother Pty Ltd

Operable Wall .... Rintouls

Toilet Partitions .... Building Plastics

Roller Shutter .... Thompson=S Roller Shutters

Waste Shutes .... Alukram

Precast Photo. Moat/ Tree Pits .... Csr Humes

Floor Sweeping .... All Areas Sweeping And Scrubbing Services

Escalator Cladding .... C.d. Townsend

Outbuildings .... Vmf Holdings

Arena Civil .... Walker Civil Engineering

North & South Lower Tier .... Csr Limited

Precinct Paving .... Sam The Paving Man

Precinct Civil .... John R Burton Contractors

Security Shutters 2, 4 & 5 .... Monarch Group Pty Ltd

Precinct Landscapes .... Design Landscapes

Shade Fabric .... Shade Structures Pacific

Demountable Lower Tier .... Aka Stage & Seating

Access Flooring .... Microfloor Systems

Not Used

Demonstration Suite Fitout .... M.A. Coleman

Acoustic Insulation .... United Insulation Contracting

Signage .... Central Signs

Serveries to Private Suite Fitout .... Curtin (Qld)

Turnstiles .... P.m.s.i. Group Pty Ltd

Resilient Flooring .... General Flooring*

Carpet .... Univers Carpets*

End Hoists .... Mannesmann Dematic Pty Ltd

Fixtures & Fittings .... Bradley Washfountain Co (Aust) Pty Ltd

Flagpoles .... Adda Flagpoles

Blinds .... Hugh Meagher & Associates

Miscellaneous Excavation .... Web Excavation

Pabx .... Siemens Gec Communications Systems

Faux Finishes .... Red Lizard

Scaffolding .... Comscaff

Granite Tops .... Original Stone

Entry Mats .... Ihl Trading

Master Keying .... Api Security

Appendix 5
Stadium Australia workers

Scheduled here are the names of those who worked together to bring the Stadium Australia dream to reality. (These names are from the Multiplex site access records.)

ABARCA, LUIS
ABBOTT, RICHARD
ABBOTT, STEVEN
ABBOTTSMITH, JIM
ABDAL, SAMIR
ABDEL, WILLIAM
ABDOO, PETER
ABDUL KADER, MOHMOUD
ABDUL-AZIZ, IBRAHIM
ABELA, STEPHEN
ABOUSCHMIESS, HASAN
ABRAHAMS, BRADLEY
ABREU, JOAO
ABREU, FRANCISCO
ABRLIC, STEVE
ABU ZALAF, ABDUL
ACCARDO, MATTEO
ACKERMAN, GRAHAM
ACKERMAN, REGINALD
ACKERMAN, HARRY PETER
ACKLAND, MATTHEW
ADAIR, ADAM
ADAM, ROBERT
ADAM, TOMA
ADAMIEC, JOHN
ADAMS, DAVID
ADAMS, ASHLEIGH
ADAMS, ROBERT
ADAMS, STEVEN
ADAMS, IAN
ADAMS, MARK
ADAMS, SCOTT
ADAMSON, GARY
ADAMUS, JAREK
ADEMOVIC, ANTHONY
ADLER, KAREN
ADRIAANS, PETER
ADRIAANS, ROBERT
AFONSO, ADOLFO
AFRIQUE, TYRONE
AGUDELO, ERNESTO
AHERN, MIKE
AHERN, STEPHEN
AHMIT, MUSTAFA
AHU, MAC
AIDONE, MARK
AIELLO, MANUEL
AINSWORTH, DENNIS WILLIAM
AINSWORTH, CRAIG

AINSWORTH, MARK JAMES
AKED, CLAYTON
AKL, CHARLES
AKUIOA, SAIA
ALAMEDDINE, RAY
ALAVANJA, DRAGAN
ALEFOSIO, LUI
ALEGERIA, HUGO
ALEKSANDROFF, ANATOLY
ALEXANDER, PAUL
ALEXANDER, SHANE
ALEXANDER, JOHN
ALEXANDER, FRANK DAMON
ALEXANDROFF, TONY
ALEXION, ELEFTHERIOS
ALFIERI, ABELARDO
ALFONZO, LIDIA
ALFRED, CRISTIAN
ALGER, MALCOLM
ALGORRY, FERNANDO FLAVIO
ALI, BASSEM
ALIM, DOMINGO
ALLAN, NATHAN
ALLAN, BEN
ALLCHIN, CHRISTOPHER
ALLEN, DARREN
ALLEN, PETER
ALLEN, BILL
ALLEN, PAUL
ALLEN, PETER
ALLEN, MATHEW
ALLEN, GREG
ALLISON, KEVIN
ALLISON, KEVIN
ALLISTON, PHILIP
ALLSTON, DARRYL
ALLWOOD, MURRY
ALMEIDA, EDWIN
ALMEIDA, RUI
ALOMEROVIC, AHMET
ALONSO, JESUS
ALONTI, SILVANO
ALONZO, KAY
ALSLEBEN, DEREK
ALTAMURA, PAUL
ALVAREZ, MARCELO
ALVES, JULIO
ALVES, JOSE MANUEL
ALVES, ACIR
ALVIS, FERNANDO

AMARAL, MANUEL
AMERICANO, SAM
AMERICANO, RICKY
AMICO, JOSE
AMMAR, NASSER
AMORIM, LUIS
AMORIM, JOAQUIM VINHAS
AMUNDSEN, CLINTON
AMYOUNI, MAGROUF
AN, CHA TONG
ANDERSEN, STEVE
ANDERSON, MICHAEL
ANDERSON, PAUL JOHN
ANDERSON, STEVEN
ANDERSON, LIONEL
ANDERSON, SIMON
ANDERSON, MARK
ANDERSON, JAMIE
ANDERSON, BRIAN
ANDERSON, CHARLES JOHN
ANDJIC, STEVE
ANDREATA, JOHN
ANDREWARTHA, BRETT KEN
ANDREWS, PETER
ANDREWS, TERRY
ANDREWS, CHRIS
ANDRONICUS, LYNETTE
ANGELESKI, KITE
ANGELONI, ALFONSO
ANLEZARK, WAYNE
ANSARI, ASLAM
ANSLOW, PETER
ANTKOWIAK, ROMAN
ANTONIA, JOHN PAUL
ANTOUN, BASSAM
ANTOUN, WADHI
ANTOUN, GEORGE
ANTOUN, NABIL
ANTOUN, ELIAS
ANWAYA, MOSHI
AORAHIM, ATHANINOUS
APPEL, DENIS
APPLIN, STEPHEN
APPS, DARREN
APULU, MAALONA
AQUILINA, JULIAN
ARAB, RIAD
ARAKAS, MANOS
ARANEDA, RICARDO
ARAPOVIC, THOMAS

ARAVENA, LUIS
ARCHER, WILLIAM
ARCHER, DAVID
ARCHER, DANIEL
ARCHIBALD, GLEN
ARDEN, GRAEME
ARDRON, SCOTT
ARHONTAKIS, NICK
ARIOLA, CARMINE
ARKAPAW, NATHAN
ARMITT, SAM
ARMSTRONG, JONATHAN
ARMSTRONG, DAVID JOHN
ARMSTRONG, MICK
ARMSTRONG, GERARD JOSEPH
ARNOLD, CRAIG
ARNUSAITIS, ARLANDAS
ARONA, TOA
ARONA, ARERAU
ARONEY, DON
ARRELL, GREGORY HOWARD
ARRILUCEA, GIANCARLOS
ARRILUCEA, LUIS
ARRILUCEA, ELIO
ARRILUCEA, JAIME
ARTHUR, IAN
ARTHUR, JAMES
ARTUSO, GINO
ASHBY, ANDRE
ASHBY, PAUL
ASHBY, STEPHEN JOHNNY
ASHFIELD, MEGAN
ASHTON, ROBERT JOHN
ASPINALL, JOHN
ASTBURY, MARTIN IAN
ASTLES, CHRISTOPHER
ASTORECA, ISAAC
ATKINS, CRAIG
ATKINSON, ALLAN
ATKINSON, CRAIG
ATKINSON, RICHARD
ATKINSON, BRETT
ATKINSON, FRANCIS
ATTARD, MIKE
ATTARD, PAUL
ATURRAETA, OSCAR
AUDSLEY, NEIL
AUIMATAGI, RICHARD
AUKINO, TEARIKI
AULICH, GEOFFREY
AUMOANA, FILIFILIA
AURISICCHIO, ANTONIO
AUSTIN, JOHN
AUSTIN, STEPHEN
AVATI, JAMES G
AVENDANO, MERCEDES
AVERY, CLIVE
AVERY, WILLIAM

AVGETIDIS, EMMANUEL
AVGETIOIS, EMMANUEL
AVGETIOIS, ZISSI-GEORGE
AVILA, JOHN
AVIS, ADRIAN NEIL
AXAM, MICHAEL
AXFORD, JOSHUA
AXOUGAS, NICK
AYALA, RALPH HENRY
AYALA, JOSE
AYLING, MICK
AZIZI, ABDUL
AZZOPARDI, VINCENT
BABIC, PETER
BABIC, MARKO
BABICH, MICHAEL
BACANI, JOSEF
BACCAM, TIM
BACHIR, MOUSSA
BADROV, JACOB
BAGGIOSSI, FRANCO
BAGHDADI, RASHAD
BAIDEN-AMISSAH, ISAAC
BAIGENT, MICHAEL
BAILEY, MATTHEW DAVID
BAILEY, DANIEL
BAILEY-GRAY, LONNIE
BAILLON, JEAN-PAUL
BAIRD, MICHAEL
BAJRAMI, SELJA
BAKER, ANDREW
BAKER, JOHN
BAKER, BILLY-JOEL
BAKER, JOHN
BALANGUE, MICHAEL
BALCKBURNE, GARRY
BALDWIN, WILLIAM RUSSELL
BALDWIN, BRIAN ROY
BALESIC, ZAIM
BALGOS, TEDDY
BALL, PHILLIP
BALLANTINE, PAUL
BAMFORD, GLEN
BANDULOV, ROBERT
BANIC, GOJKO
BANIC, DENIS
BANIC, DRAGO
BANKS, SHANE MICHAEL
BANNISTER, KEITH
BANTOS, CON
BARBATANO, JOE
BARBER, ERIC
BARBER, DANIEL
BARBERA, LEONARDO
BARBERA, JOE
BARD, GRANT
BARDACZEWSKI, MEGUEL
BARDEN, ARTHUR
BARFORD, COLIN

BARKER, JOHN BARRY
BARKER, MICHAEL
BARKER, PAUL
BARKER, ROSS
BARLOW, KEITH
BARNARD, DIANNE
BARNES, GLEN JAMES
BARNES, KYLE
BARNES, MARK
BARNES, BRIAN
BARNYCZ, JASON
BAROUNIS, GEORGE
BAROUNIS, JOHN
BARR, DANIEL
BARRETO, JOSE
BARRETT, GRAEME
BARRETT, PETER
BARRETT, RODNEY
BARRETT, MICHAEL PATRICK
BARRETT, STEPHEN GEORGE
BARRINGTON, DARREN
BARRIOS, MARIO JOSE
BARRIOS, CARLOS NELSON
BARRS, KEVIN
BARRY, MICHAEL
BARRY, REBECCA
BARTEL, MARK ANDREW
BARTLETT, GARY
BARTLETT, ALLEN
BARTOLOMEO, SORRENTINO
BARTOLOTTA, HORIS
BARTON, SHANE
BARWELL, NICHOLAS
BASIC, PAUL
BASKETT, TERENCE
BASSAL, FADI
BASSAL, ABDUL HADI
BASSAL, EDDY
BASSAL, MOHAMED
BASSETT, MICK
BASTOS VICENTE, ANTONIO
BASUKOSKI, DANIEL
BATCHELOR, JAMES
BATES, WILLIAM
BATEUP, ROSS
BATEUP, TODD
BATT, DANNY RUSSELL
BATTI, GEORGE
BATTI, TONY
BAUCE, FRANK
BAUMER, JOSEPH
BAUTOVICH, NEDO
BAXTER, PETER MARSHALL
BAYLISS, TONY
BAYLISS, GAVIN
BAZZI, ALI
BAZZI, HASSAN
BEACH, JASON LEE
BEACHUS, GARETH EDWARD

BEARCOCK, TONY JOHN
BEARD, STANLEY
BEARD, TONY ALAN
BEARD, DALE
BEASLEY, DEREK ALBERT
BEATON, MARTYN
BEATTIE, PETER
BEATTY, PAUL
BEATY, SEAN
BEAUMONT, GLENN
BEAVER, BRETT
BECCI, MARK
BECERRA, CHRISTIAN
BECHARA, RAYMOND
BECKETT, BRIAN
BECKINGHAM, JAMIE
BEDFORD, PETER ROSS
BEDFORD, DARREN
BEDFORD, KEVIN
BEDFORD, ALAN
BEDROSSIAN, SHAVARSH
BEEKMEYER, STUART
BEGG, ALFRED
BEGIC, IBRO
BEHARRELL, DAVID
BEITELIS, PAUL
BEKER, FLLOZA
BELL, LENNIE RAYMOND
BELL, GLENN
BELL, RON
BELL, MATTHEW
BELL, CHRISTOPHER ROBERT
BELLAMY, SHANON
BELLAMY, ANDREW
BELLGROVE, ADAM BERNARD
BENGSTON, CRAIG
BENKOVIC, JOHN
BENNATI, ALAN
BENNETT, WAYNE
BENNETT, JASON
BENSCH, MARTIN
BENTON, MARK
BENTUELZEN, FRANK
BEOTICH, BRUNO
BERECRY-SMITH, LIONEL
BERGIN, SEAMUS
BERLYN, NICK
BERONIC, ANTON
BERRELL, PAUL
BERRY, DAVE
BERTRAND, DEANE
BETLAND, STEVEN
BETTENSON, ADAM
BEVANDA, DAVORIN
BEZEK, IVO
BHANJI, OLIVE
BIASIOL, DAMIEN
BICANIN, ZORAN
BIDEAU, MALCOLM

BIEGEL, ROBIN
BIGGS, ADRIAN
BIGGS, TREVOR
BIGHETTI, LUIGI
BILAJAC, MIRZET
BILAJAC, FIKRET
BILAJAC, IZET
BILAJIEDEVA, AHNATUOLI
BILLINGHAM, STEVEN
BING, JASON
BINGHAM-HALL, PATRICK
BINOUSHI, MICK
BIRCH, FRANK
BIRCH, WAYNE
BIRD, MARK
BIRDS, DAVID
BIRKBECK, CRAIG
BIRKIC, NIKOLA
BIRKIC, DILKO
BIRKWOOD, MATTHEW
BISBY, RAYMOND
BISHOP, PETER
BISOGLIO, MARCO
BISWAS, SANTANU
BIVIANO, JACK
BIZZANELLI, ANDREW
BLACK, JOHN
BLACKBURN, GARY
BLACKER, MALCOLM HAROLD
BLACKHURST, TERRY
BLACKHURST, TROY
BLACKHURST, JAMES
BLACKMAN, BRADDON
BLAIR, MARK
BLAKE, SCOTT
BLANCH, BYRON
BLANCO, HECTOR
BLAND, PETER
BLANEY, FELIM
BLANNING, PETER
BLANUSA, BILL
BLEASDALE, ANTHONY JOHN
BLEASDALE, NICHOLAS KEVIN MICHAEL
BLEASDALE, NINA
BLEGG, DONALD
BLUES, ALAN HENRY
BLUNDELL, JOHN ALAN
BLUNT, DEAN
BLYTON, IAN
BOATFIELD, ANDREW
BODDY, MALCOLM
BODE, CAMERON
BOGADI, ANTUN
BOGGS, SCOTT
BOGOSAVLJEVIC, ALEX
BOGOVAC, BOGDAN
BOILA, JOHN
BOJORGE, RODRIGO

BOKALAWELA, PARA
BOLAMATU, PAUL
BOLAND, ANTHONY JOSEPH
BOLDEN, JOHN
BOLJEVIC, ALEX
BOLTE, DEAN
BOLTON, BRAD
BOLZAN, DANIEL
BONAR, FRANK
BOND, IAN
BOND, DAVID EDWIN
BONFIELD, DARRYL
BONFIELD, GLEN
BONITO, GABRIEL
BONNEY, CLINT
BOOTH, WAYNE
BORG, DEREK
BORG, NICHOLAS
BORG, JOE
BORG, STUART
BORG, STEPHEN
BORGER, SHAWN JASON
BORGER, NATHAN
BORN, RODNEY
BOROJEVIC, BRANKO
BOROVAC, PETER
BORTHWICK, DARRIN JAMES
BOSS, STEPHEN JOHN
BOUHOUTSOS, GEORGE
BOUHOUTSOS, NICK
BOUKOUVALAS, CHRISTOS
BOUSFIELD, TONY
BOUTH, SAVY
BOVA, JON
BOWDEN, KENTON
BOWLES, ANDREW JOHN
BOWMAN, DARREN
BOWMAN, FIONA
BOWTELL, ROM
BOXALL, JIM
BOYD, BRIAN
BOYD, HERMAN
BOYD, DANIEL
BOYD, STEPHEN
BOYD-SKINNER, PETER JAMES
BOYLE, WILLIAM JOHN
BOYS, TERRY JAMES
BOYS, LARRY KEITH
BOZANIC, SLOBODAN
BRADDICK, BEN
BRADFORD, SHAUN
BRADFORD, PETER
BRADFORD, RODNEY
BRADLEY, STEPHEN
BRADNEY, BRIAN PETER
BRADNEY, BRETT
BRADY, MATT
BRADY, MICHAEL
BRADY, TIM

BRAME, MARK ANTHONY
BRAMHAM, KERRY
BRAND, KENNETH RONALD
BRASILE, PAUL
BRASILE, JOHN
BRAVAR, JOHN
BRAY, VALERIE ELIZABETH
BRAY, STEPHEN LESLIE
BRCIC, JOSEPH ANDREW
BRCIC, IVAN
BRCIC, IVAN
BREEN, PETER KENNETH
BREEN, PAUL
BREIA, CHARLIE
BRENNAN, SIMON
BRENNAN, STEPHEN
BRENNAN, FRANK
BRENNAN, MARK
BRENNAN, CHRISTIAN
BRENNAN, PETER
BRENNAN, JOSEPH
BRENNAN, AARON
BRETT, PETER JOHN
BREUS, JASON
BRIDGE, DAVID
BRIDGE, JOHN LESLIE
BRIDGE, SHANE
BRIEN, DAVID MICHAEL
BRIEN, DEAN
BRIGHAM, IAN
BRIGHT, CRAIG
BRIJESKI, DENNIS
BRILLO, JOHN
BRINKLEY, SEAN
BRISCAS, GIOVANNI
BRISCHS, MICHELE
BRITTON, PETER
BROACH, LES
BROADHURST, FREDERICK F
BROADRICK, CORY JAMES
BROATCH, ALFRED JAMES
BROCKMAN, NIGEL
BRODRICK, KENNETH
BROOKER, PAUL
BROOKES, ALLEN JOHN
BROOKS, JASON
BROPHY, MARK
BROSNAHAN, CHARLES JOSEPH
BROUW, TIM
BROWN, PETER
BROWN, IAN
BROWN, IAN
BROWN, MICHAEL JAMES
BROWN, GEORGE
BROWN, PAUL
BROWN, MICHAEL JOHN
BROWN, MICHAEL
BROWN, GARY

BROWN, ANTHONY
BROWN, ERIC
BROWN, GARRY
BROWN, ROBERT
BROWN, CHRISTOPHER
BROWN, DALE
BROWN, BARRY
BROWN, DESMOND
BROWN, KEITH WILLIAM
BROWN, NIGEL
BROWN, KRISTINE
BROWN, MAX
BROWN, PETER
BROWNE, MICK
BROWNE, MICHAEL
BROWNHILL, SAM
BRUCE, CHRISTOPHER
BRUCE, PAUL
BRUMFIELD, MAL
BRUMMITT, JAMES
BRUMMITT, STEPHEN
BRUMMITT, GARY JAMES
BRUNDALL, JAMIE
BRUNETE, FRANK
BRUNNING, IAN
BRYANT, COLIN
BRYANT, GREGORY
BRYANT, ADRIAN
BRYANT, ADRIAN MATTHEW
BRZOSON, ALLAN
BUBB, BRIAN
BUBB, ADRIAN
BUCHANAN, COLIN
BUCHEL, MATTHEW JAMES
BUCKLAND, WILLIAM MILLMAN
BUCKLEY, KEVIN
BUCKLEY, TRENT
BUERCKNER, REGINALD
BUGARIJA, KRISTO
BUGARIJA, JOSIP
BUGDEN, ANDREW
BUGEJA, GREG
BUHAC, MILLIE
BUIJS, ALEX
BUITRAGO, HARVEY
BUJEWICZ, EDDIE
BUKOVAC, STAIKO
BULLEN, ANTHONY
BULLOCH, ALEXANDER
BUN, SIPHALLA
BUNCOMBE, GREGORY
BURCHELL, ALAN
BURGE, GLEN
BURGESS, MATTHEW
BURGOS, EDUARDO
BURGOS, RICHARD
BURKE, ANTHONY JAMES
BURKE, GARRY

BURKE, KEVIN
BURKINSHAW, SHANNON
BURLING, ROBERT
BURMAN, RICHARD
BURMUDZIJA, DAMIR
BURNER, RICHARD
BURNETT, DAVID
BURNETT, ANGUS
BURNETT, COLIN PETER
BURNETT, IAN
BURNITT, WAYNE
BURNS, GREGORY JOHN
BURNS, GERARD
BURNS, DAVID
BURNS, PETER
BURTON, PAUL
BURTON, CHRIS
BUSCALL, DONALD
BUSSELL, CHAD
BUTLER, BRENDAN
BUTLER, RUSSELL
BUTLER, ROY
BUTLER, GEOFFREY
BUTLER, ANTHONY
BUTT, BRAD
BYE, NEVILLE
BYRNE, TONY
BYRNE, ROBIN
BYRNES, HOWARD
BYRNES, MARK
CACCIAPAGLIA, SALVATORE
CACERES, LUISA
CADDEY, GRAHAM
CADDEY, JOHN MORTIMER
CADILE, ANTONIO
CAIN, ALEXANDER
CAIN, TROY
CAIN, JASON
CAIRES, JOSE
CAIRNS, LYALL
CAIRNS, PAUL
CALABRESE, GIUSEPPE
CALIMQUIM, ANTONIO
CALLAGHAN, NATHAN
CALLAGHAN, BRIAN DENNIS
CALMASINI, RENATO
CALNAN, JACK
CALVARESI, REMO
CAMERON, NEIL
CAMILLERI, LAURIE
CAMILLERI, CHARLES
CAMILLERI, CHARLES
CAMILLERI, EDWARD
CAMM, DARRELL
CAMMANO, PATRICK
CAMPBELL, TIMOTHY HAMILTON
CAMPBELL, RON
CAMPBELL, DAVID B

CAMPBELL, TREVOR
CAMPBELL, WADE
CAMPBELL, TONY
CAMPBELL, MALCOLM
CAMPBELL, SEAN
CAMPBELL, STEPHEN
CAMPBELL, LOUISE
CAMPBELL, GARRY
CAMPBELL, STEWART
CAMPIONE, ALBERTO SAM
CAMPOS, ANTONIO
CANAL, GREG
CANDY, WAYNE
CANELLIS, ALAN
CANNAVO, ROSS
CANNING, JIM
CANNISTRA, JOE
CANNIZZARO, SEBASTION
CANNON, SHANE
CANTY, GLEN
CANU, DANIEL
CAO, BOB
CAPDEVILA, NICOLAS
CAPITANI, REMO
CAPITANI, DAVID
CAPITANI, AUGUSTO
CAPIZZI, JOE
CAPPADONA, TOM
CAPPER, ROGER
CAPUTO, SALUATORE
CAPUTO, CALOGERO
CARBERRY, JAMES
CARDAMONE, FRANCESCO
CARDE, STEPHEN
CARDILE, RINALDO
CARDILLO, STEPHEN
CAREY, PATRICK
CAREY, DECLAN
CAREY, JOHN
CAREY, KEVIN
CARIOLATO, ADOLFO
CARLEY, GARY
CARLINO, RICK
CARMINE, EUGENE
CARMONT, MICHAEL
CARNEIRO, SIDNEY
CARNEY, RODNEY PAUL
CARNEY, ANDREW
CARNIATO, ALFEO
CARNIATO, PAOLO
CARR, JOHN PETER
CARR, PHILLIP ALLAN
CARR, JEREMY JUN
CARRASCO, VICTOR
CARRASCO, JAMIE ANTONIO
CARREY, ADAM
CARROLL, EDWARD
CARROLL, MICHAEL
CARROLL, DAWN CATHERINE
CARROLL, BERNARD

CARROLL, PATRICK
CARROLL, CHRIS
CARROLL, CHRIS
CARROLL, ANTHONY
CARTA, PHILLIP
CARTHEW, NEIL
CARTISANO, MICHAEL
CARTLEDGE, RODNEY DALL
CARTWRIGHT, PAUL
CARTWRIGHT, DARIUS
CARVALHEIRO, MANUEL MARTINS
CARVALHO, CARLOS
CARWANA, JOHN
CASA, EPIFAYIO
CASEY, CARL
CASIMATY, FRANK
CASIMIRO, ANTONIO
CASON, CHRISTIAN
CASS, PHILLIP
CASSAR, NEIL
CASSIDY, ALEX
CASSIN, ANTHONY
CASSISI, VITO
CASTILLO, FRANK
CASTILLO, JOSEPH
CASTILLO, FRANK
CATALANO, ROSARIO
CATHAL, MCCLOSKEY
CATLETT, GREGORY
CATROPPA, CARLOS ALBERTO
CAULCUTT, DAVID
CAVANAGH, LARRY
CAVE, ROSS
CAVICCHIA, GIUSEPPE
CAWLEY, MATTHEW JOHN
CAWLEY, PETER
CAZZOLLI, CAMILLO
CAZZY, JOHN
CEBALLOS, MANUEL
CEFAI, DAVID
CEFAI, JOSEPH
CEKO, RANKO
CENTINDAG, KENAN
CEPEDA, ANDRES
CERIC, SAMIR
CHAALAN, ABBAS
CHADWICK, THOMAS
CHADWICK, DEBORAH
CHAFFEY, CHRISTIAN
CHAHINE, GEORGE
CHALHOUB, GEORGE
CHALLENDOR, CLAYTON
CHALLENOR, JAMES
CHALMERS, ROBERT
CHALON, ERIC JACQUES
CHAMBERS, ROBERT
CHAMPION, CORMAC
CHAN, KWOK KEUNG

CHAN, DANIEL
CHAND, MUKESH
CHANG, DOO HAK
CHANG YANG, LEE
CHANNELLS, ADAM
CHANNON, JOHN
CHANNON, JAMES
CHANT, BRIAN
CHAPE, CHRIS
CHAPLIN, JIM
CHAPMAN, CHRISTOPHER JOHN
CHAPMAN, GAVIN
CHAPMAN, ANTHONY
CHAPMAN, MAXWELL KEITH
CHAPMAN, RAYMOND
CHAPMAN, ALAN
CHAPMAN, ANDREW
CHAPMAN, ANDREW
CHAPPELL, GARY
CHARAF, BORHAN
CHARAN, JAI RAM
CHARLTON, IAN
CHARLTON, NEVILLE
CHATTO, CRAIG
CHEETHAM, KEN
CHEN, PEI
CHENEY, CRAIG
CHENEY, JUSTIN
CHENEY, TRENT
CHENG, RITHY
CHENG, MANY
CHENG, BANDOL
CHERRY, TODD
CHESSELL, MARTIN
CHEW, XIAXIN
CHEW, SIMON
CHEYNE, COLIN LESLIE
CHICCA, ROBERT
CHILBY, GRAHAM
CHIN, MONG CHING
CHISHOLM, MICK
CHO, SEOUNG MAN
CHO, HYUN-JOON
CHO, JONG-JOON
CHO, SEUNG-KOO
CHOI, KYOUNG HO
CHOI, EUN KYOO
CHOI, OANG KYOO
CHOI, HOI JIN
CHOI, YOON SEOK
CHRISTIE, TRENT
CHRISTIE, ROBERT
CHU, CHIE THENG
CHUDOBA, JONATHAN
CHUI, JIAO CUI
CHUNG, MICHAEL
CHURCH, MICHAEL JOHN
CHURCHILL, CHAS

CHURCHILL, PAUL
CIARCIELLO, SAM
CINDRIC, JOHN
CINI, CARMELLO
CIRAOLO, PAUL
CIRAOLO, ADAM
CLARK, PHILIP
CLARK, ETHAN-JOSEPH
CLARK, STEPHEN
CLARK, SHANE
CLARK, WILLIAM
CLARK, GLEN
CLARK, ROGER
CLARK, GEOFFREY
CLARK, JOHN ANDREW
CLARK, KAREN
CLARKE, CHRIS
CLARKE, MATTHEW
CLARKE, GLEN
CLARKE, STEPHEN
CLARKE, ROBERT
CLARKE, MAX
CLARKE, KEN
CLARKE, JAMES
CLARKE, NOEL
CLARKE, DAVID
CLARKSON, STEVEN
CLASPER, NEVILLE
CLASPER, DENIS
CLASPER, ADAM
CLAXTON, DENNIS
CLAYSON, DARREN
CLEAR, PATRICK
CLEARY, ALLEN CHARLES
CLEAVE, DAREN
CLEGG, DWANE
CLEMM, LENNIE
CLEWS, JOHN
CLIFFORD, JOHN
CLIFTON, ROBERT
CLISDELL, MARK
CLOSE, MIKE
CLOUT, MICHAEL JAMES
CLOUT, JEFF
CLUSS, TROY
COATES, DAVID
COBETA, ALBERTO
COBURN, SHANNON
COCCA, FRANK
COCHRAN, STAN
COCHRAN, JOSEPH
COCHRANE, ANNA MARGARET
COCKERILL, DARREN
COCKROFT, GARY
COCKS, ALAN
COE, CHRIS
COELHO, JOE
COELHO, MARTIN

COFFEY, ROSS
COFFEY, DARRAGH
COKER, DARRYL
COLBOURNE, BRETT DAVID
COLE, DARREN
COLE, PHILLIP
COLEGRAVE, ALAN LESLIE
COLEMAN, PHILLIP DARREN
COLEMAN, CRAIG
COLEMAN, STEPHEN
COLEMAN, TIMOTHY
COLERIDGE, MERVYN
COLES, PHILLIP JOHN
COLES, CHRISTIAN
COLL, AUSTIN
COLLESS, DAVID
COLLETT, WILLIAM JOSEPH
COLLETT, ROBERT
COLLETT, RAYMOND
COLLIER, EDWARD
COLLINS, MARK
COLLIS, TODD
COLLISON, DAVID
COLUSSI, ANDREA
COMBER, FRANK
COMELLO, ALLAN
COMINOS, MARIA
COMMINS, CHRIS
COMMISSIONE, VINCENT ROBERT
CONDON, STEVE
CONEFERY, MATTHEW
CONNELL, DOUGLAS KENNETH
CONNELL, BERNARD DANIEL
CONNELL, RICHARD
CONNELL, RORY ADAM
CONNELLAN, STEVE
CONNER, PETER
CONROY, TOM
CONROY, EVAN
CONSOLINO, ANTHONY
CONSTABLE, BEN
COOK, GEOFFREY
COOK, TREVOR
COOK, DON
COOK, STEPHEN
COOK, SHANE
COOK, PHILLIP
COOKSLEY, DAVID
COOMBES, ANTHONY
COOMBES, SCOTT
COOMBES, REGINALD JAMES
COONEY, ROBERT
COOPER, ADAM
COOPER, MATTHEW
COOPER, JASON
COOPER, PHILLIP
COOPER, JAMES

COOTE, BRUCE COLLIN
COPE, JOHN KENNETH
COPLESTONE, DENNIS
CORBETT, CRAIG
CORBETT, ASHLEY
CORCOGLIONITI, FRANK
CORDA, TOM
CORKE, NOEL
CORKE, IAN
CORKERY, GEOFF
CORNISH, PETER WARREN
CORREIA, GASPAR
CORREIA, SILVIO
CORREIA, MICHAEL DE SOUSA
CORREIA, JAMES
CORRY, DAVID
CORTEZ, WALTER
CORVALAN, CARLOS
COSCARELLA, CORRADO
COSO, MILORAD
COSTA, FRANCISCO
COSTA, ANTONIO
COSTA, JOAQUIM
COSTELLO, NIGEL
COSTELLO, BRUCE EDWARD
COSYAN, CUNEYT
COTTER, TAMIHANA JASON
COTTERILL, GRAHAM
COUGHLAN, PATRICK
COURTWOOD, JIM
COUSINS, RHYS
COUSINS, PETER
COUSINS, TONY
COUTO SCHOLZ, MARCIO RICARDO
COVENEY, FRANKLIN A
COVENY, COLIN
COWLEY, CHRIS
COWLEY, MARK
COX, VINCENT
COX, PAUL RICHARD
COX, RON
COYLE, GERRY
COYLE, DAVID JOHN
COYNE, SEAN
COYTE, CRAIG
CRAIG, JAMES WILLIAM
CRANE, CHRIS
CRANE, TERRY
CRANGLE, PATRICK
CREALY, ALLEN
CREAMER, PERI MARK
CREAN, JOHN
CREIGHTON, DARYL
CREIGHTON, JOSHUA
CREMASCO, GEOVANI
CRIPPS, GLENN
CRISMALE, GINO

CRISMALE, JOE
CRISTOFARO, TONY
CRNOKRAK, JOVAN
CROCKFORD, JASON
CROFT, SHANE
CROFT, GLENN ALLAN
CROFT, KEN
CROFT, DAVID
CROMBIE, ALEX TITA
CROMBIE, KEN
CRONE, ROBERT
CRONIN, MICHAEL
CROOKS, WILLIAM
CROOKS, WILLIAM STANLEY
CROOKS, GARY
CROWLEY, STEPHEN
CROWLEY, MICHAEL
CROWLEY, CAMERON
CROWLEY, TOM
CRUICKSHANK, TOBY
CRUZ, HECTOR
CRUZ, ARMANDO
CUFF, TERENCE
CUFF, TERENCE
CUFFE, BRIAN
CUI, TAI JING
CUKAR, TOM
CUKON, ADRIANO
CULGAN, CHRISTOPHER
CULICAN, JOSEPH
CULLEN, KEITH LESLIE
CULLEN, LUKE
CULLEN, IAN JAMES
CULLEN, KEVIN
CULLEN, MARK
CUMMING, PETER
CUMMINGS, JOHN
CUMMINGS, RAYMOND
CUMMINGS, KELVIN
CUMMINS, STEVEN
CUNDY, NIGEL
CUNNIFFE, DENNIS
CUNNINGHAM, DAMIAN
CUNNINGHAM, MARK
CUNNINGHAM, PETER
CUNNINGHAM, JAMES
CUPAC, RADOVAN
CUPAC, MIROSLAV
CUPAC, RADE
CUPAC, STEVAN
CUPAC, BOSKO
CUPAC, PETAR
CUPAC, MOMCILO
CUPAC, DRAGO
CUPAC, SINISA
CUPAC, BRANKO
CUPAC, JOVAN
CUPITT, LENNARD
CUPLOV, ERMIN

CUPO, DANNY
CURAN, WES
CURMI, MARCO
CURRAN, PATRICK
CURRIE, BRETT
CURRIE, ANDREW
CUSACK, PETER BRENDEN
CUSACK, SIMON
CUTHBERTSON, MICHAEL
CVETICANIN, NICK
CVETICANIN, MICHAEL
CZOCH, KAKUB
D'ALESSANDRO, VINCENT
D'AMATO, DOMINIC
D'ANDRETI, ENRICO
D'ANDRETI, JOSEPH
D'ACUNTO, LOUIE
DA COSTA, FERNANDO
DA ROS, MARIO
DA RUOS, JOSEPH
DA SILVA, CARLOS HUMBETO
DA SILVA, MARIO
DA SILVA, PAULO
DA SILVA, DELMIRO
DA SILVA QUINTAL, HORACIO
DABLIZ, ABDUL-A
DABROWSKI, ZBIGNIEW
DACOSTA, GAVIN
DAE HAK, YOO
DAGG, GARY
DAGGER, ROBERT
DAGLISH, STEVEN
DAHDAH, RABIH
DAHDAH, ROBIN
DAIS, JUARES
DAKIN, CHRIS
DALCHIRANIS, PHIL
DALCIN, GILDO
DALE, TERRY
DALEY, NICK
DALEY, MICHAEL
DALLA LIBERA, ROBERT
DALMATI, FRANK
DALRYMPLE, WILLIAM
DALTON, PATRICIA
DALTON, JOHN
DALY, JERRY
DALY, SIMON
DAMIR, ZONIC
DAMJANOVIC, IVAN
DAMJANOVIC, BOB
DANDACHLI, ALI
DANIELS, MARK
DANIELS, RUSSELL
DANKS, GEORGE
DARBY, GRAHAM
DARBY, GARY
DARCY, BRYAN
DARLOW, HARVEY

DAROS, FRANK
DAVID, CAESAR
DAVIDSON, DERRICK
DAVIE, JOHN CHARLES
DAVIE, ROD
DAVIES, GARY
DAVIES, JOHN
DAVIES, ROBERT
DAVIES, DAVID JOHN
DAVIES, JAMES
DAVINO, JOE
DAVIS, GARRY JAMES
DAVIS, PETER
DAVIS, GUY
DAVIS, COLIN
DAW, GEOFFREY
DAWES, RODNEY
DAWES, MICHAEL
DAWKING, COLIN ALBERT
DAWS, KYM
DAWSON, EUGENE
DAWSON, PAUL
DAWSON, DANIEL
DAY, ANDREW PATRICK
DAY, PETER
DAY, BRIAN PATRICK
DAY, BRETT
DE ARAGAO, OSCAR
DE BILBE, LEVI
DE CARVALHO, ADIRSON
DE CARVALHO, LUIZ EDUARDO
DE CARVALHO, SERGIO
DE COSTA, JOAQUIM
DE FILIPPIS, ALBERTO
DE FREITAS, ROY
DE GRUCHY, SIMON
DE MARTIN, GLEN
DE MISKIC, MISHA
DE NUNTIIS, PIERO
DE OLIVEIRA, CAMILO
DE SILVA, AUGUSTO
DE SILVA, LUIS
DE SOUZA, JOSE CARLOS
DE ST GERMAIN, DAMIEN
DE VROOME, JOHN
DEACON, ALLAN
DEAKIN, DAVID
DEAN, GALEA?
DEANE, JOHN
DEANE, BRUCE
DEARLING, DAVID
DEBATTISTA, GODWIN
DEBONO, RODNEY
DEETH, PHILIP
DEGUARA, MARK
DEIGNAN, ALAN
DEKU, NOA
DEL PINTO, FRANCO

DELAHUNTY, RICHARD JOSEPH
DELANEY, MARTIN
DELANEY, DEREK
DELANOUE, STEVEN
DELGADO, PEDRO
DELL'OREFICE, CAMILLO
DELLA, DANNY
DELLA-CHOPPA, DANNY
DELLAR, ROBERT
DELLAR, PETER
DELLARTE, TONY
DELLER, DAVID
DEMILIO, JOHN
DEMMEL, RICHARD
DENDLE, TRENT
DENHOLM, ROBERT
DENHOLM, NEIL
DENNESS, JIM
DENNESS, STUART
DENNEY, JAMES
DENNING, STEVE
DENNIS, WAYNE
DENNIS, TERRY
DENNIS, TERENCE
DENNIS, WAYNE
DENOON, ROY
DENT, SIMOM
DENT, RICKY
DENT, MATTHEW
DENTON, DANIEL
DEROME, LES
DEROME, BRETT
DESINAN, BRUNO
DESMOND, SHANE
DEVENNEY, PATRICK
DEVIC, BRANKO
DEVLIN, MARK
DEWHIRST, WAYNE
DEWSTOW, GRAHAM JOHN
DIANA, PETER
DIAS, ADELINO
DIAS, RUI
DIAS, EVARISTO
DIAVATIOTIS, DIMITRIOS JIM
DIAZ, NESTOR
DICK, BOB
DICKER, GEOFFERY
DICKERSON, PHILLIP
DICKFORD, JOHN
DICKINSON, MARK
DICKSON, ROBERT
DICOMUN, SERAFINE JOSEPH
DIDOVICH, ARTHUR

DIDOVICH [LAMPSONS], PAUL
DIFFORD, RICHARD JOHN
DIGANNI, ROBERT
DIGIROLAMO, ANTHONY
DIGRANDE, ENRICO
DIKIC, TOM
DIMACALI, DANNY
DIMERY, GAVIN
DIMITAR, TODOROVSKI
DIMITRAKAKIS, JIM
DIMITROVSKI, MICHAEL "ROLLY"
DINATALE, ANGELO
DINGWALL, MARK
DINH, DUC THANG
DINNERVILLE, DOUGLAS
DINWOODE, GLEN
DIPPEL, JASON
DIRCKS, BEN
DIVICH, GRANT
DIXON, KEITH
DIXON, CRAIG
DIXON, ROD
DJAKOVIC, BRANKO
DJAKOVIC, VELJKO
DJAKOVIC, DINKO
DJURISIC, ZORAN
DJURISIC, SPASOJE
DMYTRUK, MARTIN
DO CARMO, NORMANDO
DOBBIE, BARRY
DOBING, STEPHEN
DOBINSON, DARRIN
DODD, BRADLEY ALAN
DOHERTY, CONNER
DOHERTY, JOHN
DOHERTY, PETER
DOIC, BORIS
DOLLARD, EUGENE
DOMINGUEZ, HUGO
DONAGHEY, MARK
DONAGHY, KEITH
DONALD, ROBERT
DONEGAN, MARK
DONEGAN, HARRY
DONELLAN, SHAYNE
DONNELLY, CHRISTOPHER
DONOGHUE, TERENCE
DONOHOE, EDWARD
DOOLAN, MICHAEL JOHN
DOOLEY, TOM
DOS SANTOS, WAGNER
DOS SANTOS, JOSE
DOUGLAS, IVAN
DOUGLAS, MARTY
DOUGLAS, COLIN WILLIAM

DOUGLAS, WILLIAM JAMES
DOVGAN, TONY
DOWER, ANDREW
DOWLING, DOM
DOWLING, GRAHAM WAYNE
DOWN, GREG
DOWNES, SCOTT JAMES
DOWNES, TROY
DOWNES, SEAN
DOWNEY, DANNY
DOWNEY, DARRAN
DOWNTON, DENIS REGINALD
DOWSE, SHANE
DOYLE, FERGUS
DOYLE, CHRISTOPHER
DOYLE, DANNY
DRAKOULIS, STEVEN
DRANSFIELD, SCOTT
DRCA, RADOVAN
DRCA, MARINKO
DRCA, SMILYANA
DREWE, MERVYN LESLIE
DRIES, JOHN
DRING-REID, PETER
DROVER, IAN SEAN
DRUERY, SCOTT
DRUMMOND, JO
DUBROJA, JOVAN
DUCKERING, SHAYNE
DUCKETT, BOB
DUFF, PETER
DUFFY, ANTHONY PETER
DUFFY, SHANE
DUFFY, COLIN
DUGGAN, STEPHEN
DUGGAN, MARC
DUGGAN, NICHOLAS
DUGGAN, DENIS
DUHERIC, AHMET
DUHERIC, NERMILIA
DUIC, TOM
DUKIC, DON
DUMIC, ALEKSANDAR
DUNAJCIK, MICHAEL
DUNBAR, BARRY
DUNCAN, DANIEL
DUNCAN, IAN JAMES
DUNCAN, JONATHAN
DUNKLEY, DAVID
DUNLEA, JOHN
DUNLOP, STUART
DUNLOP, STEPHEN
DUNN, COLIN
DUNN, JACK
DUNN, WARWICK
DUNN, DARREN
DUNN, WARWICK
DUNSHEA, ANDREW JAMES
DUPOND, MICHAEL

DURBAN, JUAN
DURHAM, GRAHAM
DURIC, RUSHI
DURKAN, SEAN
DUROSE, STEPHEN
DWYER, DAMIEN
DWYER, STEPHEN
DWYER, FINTAN
DYASON, STEVE
DYER, GREG
DYKTYNSKI, NEVELLE
DYKTYNSKI, SAMUEL
DZELMANIS, PAUL
EADES, PHILIP
EAGLES, FRANK
EARNSHAW, TOM
EARP, GRAHAM
EASON, TYRONE
EASTON, DAVID
EASTWOOD, STEVEN DAVID
EBERHARD, AXEL
EDEN, MARK
EDGELOE, TYE
EDGERTON, ALAN
EDGTTON, WAYNE
EDMENDS, DAVID ERIC
EDMUNDS, SCOTT
EDWARDS, GARRY
EDWARDS, ALFRED
EDWARDS, ROSS
EDWARDS, GREG CHARLES
EE, BEN
EGAN, DAVID GEORGE
EGAN, BRENDAN
EGAN, DAMIEN
EGGINS, RODNEY
EILIAZADEH, NATAN
EIRICH, HAFIZ
EISEN, JOHN
EISHAUER, SIMON
EJJE, NAZIH
EL BEISARI, FARAJ
EL GHOUL, OMAR
EL HAGG, FADY
EL-AZZI, ROGER
EL-HAKIM, ELIE
EL-TOM, NICOLAS
ELAKAOUI, ALI
ELBIKAI, FAWAZ
ELEFANTIS, JOHN
ELIAS, SID
ELIAS, JOSE
ELIAS, VINCENT
ELISAIA, TEKAWA
ELISAIA, EDWARD
ELKIN, STEPHEN
ELLACOTT, MICHAEL
ELLERTON, ADAM
ELLINSWORTH, MICHAEL

PAUL
ELLIOTT, MATTHEW
ELLIOTT, ALAN
ELLIOTT, KIRK
ELLIOTT, STEVEN
ELLIOTT, MARK
ELLIS, JASON
ELLIS, LLOYD
ELLIS, PETER
ELLISON, BRUCE
ELRISH, MOHAMAD
ELSAYED, MICOL
ELSEGOOD, DONALD
ELSEY, KEVIN
EMERTON, DAVID
EMMANOUEL, CON
EMMANOUILIDIS, PETER
ENDEAN, MICHAEL
ENGEBRETSEN, ADRIAN
ENGLEZOU, GEORGE
ENGLISH, JOHN GEOFFREY
ENGLISH, MICHAEL JAMES
ENGVIG, STEVEN
ERCEG, SCOVKO
ERCEG, LJUBE
ERDMANIS, PETER
ERRINGTON, RICHARD JAMES
ERROFEFF, MARK
ESCALANTE, LUIS
ESMAILPOUR, MICHAEL
ESTEPHAN, JASON
ESTIGOY, RAYMOND
ETEMOVIC, SMAIL
EVANS, CECIL
EVANS, RENEE JOY
EVANS, MARK
EVANS, PHIL
EVANS, PETER CHARLES
EVANS, MARTIN
EVANS, EVA
EVANS, DAL
EVANS, DAVID
EVANS, CECIL DAVID
EVANS, PAUL
EVERSON, GARY DALE
EYLES, ROBERT
EYNDHOVEN, TROY
FABRI, RICHARD ANTHONY
FABRI, DANIEL
FABRIZIOG, RIGGIO
FAEDDA, ARMANDO
FAGHEIH SHOJAEI, HOSSEIN
FAGONE, SALVATORE
FAHY, MICHAEL
FAINT, DAVID
FAIRWEATHER, LAURENCE
FAIRWEATHER, NOEL
FAIVA, MARK
FAJLOUN, BASSIM

FAKIOLAS, SPIROS
FALANGA, JIM
FALANGA, ADAM
FALCON, ALEX
FALCON, JAVIER ANTONIO
FALEFATA, SATELE
FALLON, ANDY
FAMULARO, ROBERT
FAMULARO, PAUL
FANFONI, MARIO
FANJ, SAMIR
FANTOV, MARIO
FANTOV, DENIS
FARAH, DAVID NICHOLAS
FARDELLA, ANTHONY
FARINA, GINO
FARLEY, MICHAEL
FARMER, SCOTT MATTHEW
FARMER, ROBIN DAVID
FARMER, DAVID NATHAN
FARNON, DARRYL
FARRELL, GRAEME
FARRELL, CIARAN
FARREN, ROY
FARRUGIA, MATTHEW
FARSACI, SANTO
FARSACI, ANTONIO
FASANO, JOE
FAUL, KEVIN PATRICK
FAULKNER, AARON
FAUVETTE, JEFFREY
FAWKNER, GREG
FAY, PATRICK
FAY, KEVIN
FAY, KENNETH
FAZEKAS, MARYANNE
FEDELI, DANIEL
FEEHAM, PATRICK
FEILD, STEVE
FELTL, JOHN
FENG, PETER
FENTON, ALICK JOHN
FERGUSON, ANDREW
FERGUSON, DAVID JOHN
FERGUSON, ALAN
FERGUSON, GREGORY
FERGUSON, COLIN
FERN, GARRY
FERNANCE, DARRYL
FERNANDES, J. MARIO
FERNANDEZ, ADOLFO
FERNSTROM, ULRIKA M
FERRACCIOLI, GEOVANNI
FERRAINA, ANDRE
FERRARESE, ADAM
FERRARI, DEBRA
FERRARI, JULIO C
FERRARO, MICHAEL
FERREIRA, ROGERIO

FERREIRA, FERNANDO
OLIVEIRA
FERREIRA, CARLOS
FERREIRA, ALBINO MANUEL
FERRIN, GIANNI
FERRIS, TUMOANA
FIALA, HORST
FIDOW, FLYNN
FIERRO, JOHN
FILIPE, ARSENIO
FILIPPI, COLUMBA
FILIPPONE, IVANO
FILLERY, PETER
FILLERY, DANYEL
FILMER, COLIN
FILSHIE, PETER
FIN, ALESSANDRO
FINCH, DAVID
FINEMORE, BRUCE
FINLAYSON, ALEX
FINN, BRIAN
FINN, KIERAN
FINN, CARLEY
FINNEGAN, SEAMUS
FIODOROFF, NICK
FIORI, CLAUDE
FIRMSTONE, JOHN BERNARD
FISH, GRAHAM
FISH, GEOFFREY
FISHBURN, NEIL
FISHER, JASON
FISHER, JOHN
FISHER, AARON
FISHER, CRAIG
FITZELL, ROBERT JOHN
FITZGERALD, BARRY
FITZGERALD, VICTOR
RAYMOND
FITZPATRICK, MICHAEL
JOSEPH
FITZPATRICK, WILLIAM
FITZROY, MARK
FITZSIMONS, JAMES
FLACK, ROBERT
FLANDERS, VINCENT
FLANNIGAN, GRANT LESLIE
FLEMING, BRUCE
FLEMING, SCOTT
FLEMING, MARK
FLEMING, BROOK
FLEMING, TOD
FLETCHER, GRAEME
FLETCHER, NICHOLAS
FLETCHER, RONALD
FLORES, MICHAEL
FLORIAN, LORENZO
FLORIAN, SANDRO
FLORIAN, SILVIO
FLOWERS, CRAIG

FODOR, NICHOLAS JOHN
FOGGO, JUSTIN
FOLEY, JOHN
FOLEY, LUKE
FOLEY, GLENN
FOLEY, PETE
FONG, ALEXANDER
FONG, VICTOR
FOOTE, ANTHONY
FORBES, TERENCE NEALE
FORD, TROY
FORD, ROSS
FORD, TOBY
FORDE, PADDY
FORFOLIAS, EFFIE
FORMICA, LISA
FORREST, GRAHAM
FORSHAW, GEOFFREY
FORSHAW, COLIN
FORSTER, ROBIN
FORSTER, GLENN
FORTE, ANDREW
FOSCA, WILLIAM
FOSTER, STEPHEN
FOSTER, STEVEN CLYDE
FOSTER, MEG
FOSTER, PAUL
FOSTER, GLENN
FOSTER, ANDREW WARREN
FOTAKIS, FRANK
FOTI, ROCCO
FOUNDADJI, CRISTOS
FOX, JIM
FRADEL, CLAUDE
FRAGULIS, DAVID
FRANCE, JAMES JOSEPH
FRANCHINA, SAM
FRANCIS, LEON
FRANCIS, ADAM
FRANCISKOVIC, RENATO
FRANGS, RICHARD OWEN
FRANKLIN, STEPHEN
FRASER, ALISTAIR
FRASER, WILLIAM GORDON
FRASER, LAWRENCE
FRASER, BARRY
FRASER, LINDSAY JAMES
FRATER, KAREN
FRATINI, JAMES
FRAZER, TIM
FRAZER, GREG
FREDERICKS, JASON
FREEMAN, MARGARET
FREESTONE, DAVID
FRENCH, GARY
FRENCH, BRETT
FRENCH, JOHN
FRENCH, DAVE
FRENCH, GARY

FRENCH, KEVIN
FREUND, JASON
FREW, DAVID
FRICKE, BRUCE
FRIDAY, WAYNE
FRIPP, DENIS
FROES, MIGUEL ANGELO
FROGLEY, NOEL
FROST, PETER
FROST, ANDREW
FROST, JOHN GRAHAM
FROST, DARREN
FRUCI, VITO
FRY, MICHAEL
FRYDMAN, ALLAN
FUGLE, CHRISTOPHER
FULLER, JASON
FULLER, COLIN
FULLER, LARRY
FULLER, LARRY STEVEN
FULLER, WAYNE GLEN
FULLERTON, STEVEN
FULTON, TREVOR
FUNCH, MICHAEL
FUNG, ALAN
FURCHTMANN, MARK HANS
FURLONG, CHAD
FURNELL, GARY
FURNESS, JOHN
FURNESS, GREG
FUSCO, JOHN
GABIN, DANIEL
GABIN, JAROME
GABRIJEL, SKEC
GABRIS, TOM
GAFFANEY, CHRISTOPHER
GAGIC, SAVA
GAGIC, MILORAD
GAGIC, RANKO
GAGIC, BRANKO
GAGIC, ZELIKO
GAHAN, SHANE
GAJARDO, JUAN
GALANENA, ALEJANDRO
GALATI, GIUSSEPPE
GALE, ALAN PHILLIP
GALE, PHILLIP
GALEA, RENNIE
GALEA, MARK
GALEA, PERCY
GALEA, JASON JOSEPH
GALEA, DANIEL
GALINDO, JOEL
GALLACE, EMMANUEL
GALLACHER, STEPHEN
GALLAGHER, BRUCE
GALLAGHER, TONY
GALLAGHER, GARY
GALLANT, BRETT

GALLEN, JAMES DAVID
GALLINA, RENATO
GALOV, ADAM
GALVIN, NOEL JOHN
GALVIN, RICHARD
GAMBLE, STEPHEN
GAMBLIN, BEN
GANNON, DAVID JOHN
GARAICOA, DAVID
GARCIA, HUGO
GARCIA, RAMON
GARCIA, MANUEL
GARCIA, BLANCA
GARCIA, CARLOS
GARDINER, JAMES CHARLES
GARDINER, LUKE
GARDINER, MARK
GARDNER, BRIAN
GARDNER, ROBERT
GARLAND, PETER
GARNER, CRAIG
GARNHAM, TIMOTHY
GARNSEY, DESMOND
GARRAD, PETER
GARRAD, JOHN
GARRATT, JASON
GARRETT, KIERAN
GATEGOOD, RICHARD
GATICA, EXEQUIEL
GAUCI, JAMES
GAVAN, RICHARD
GAWLAS, MICHEAL
GAYTON, LARRY
GAZNAWI, MIRWAIS
GEARIE, MARK ANTHONY
GEDDES, NEIL
GEE, DARREN
GEE, BARRY
GEE, BRENT
GEE, DAVID
GEE, MARK
GEERING, ROBIN
GELLENDER, ANDREW
GENOVEZOS, PETER
GENTLE, BARRY
GENUA, ANTHONY
GEORGE, PETER
GEORGE, ANTHONY
GEORGE, ANTHONY
GEORGE, ANTHONY
GEORGIEVSKI, TRAJAN (TOM)
GERAKITEYS, ARTHUR
GERASIMOU, LOUIS
GERRARD, ANDREW
GERSBACH, EDWARD
GERSBACK, JASON
GHANEM, SAAD
GHANEM, YOUSSEF EID
GHANNOUM, DAVID

GHANTOUS, ZIAD
GHEZZI, RON
GIAMMARCO, AUGUSTO
GIANNOPOULOS, ARIS
GIANNOULIS, CON
GIBBONS, BRETT BRADLEY
GIBBS, FREDRICK JAMES
GIBBS, TERRENCE GEORGE
GIBSON, BENJAMIN
GIBSON, GERARD
GIBSON-BROWN, ALAN
GIEVERS, MEINOLF
GIEZEKAMP, ROBERT
GILBERT, CAMERON
GILBERT, TUI
GILBERT, NEVILLE GRAHAM
GILBERT, PAUL
GILBERT, RYAN
GILBERTSON, PAUL
GILBY, BEN
GILL, KEVIN
GILLESPIE, DAVID JOHN
GILLESPIE, PETER
GILLESPIE, JOHN
GILLETT, MARK ALEXANDER
GILLIC, JAMES JOESPH
GILLIES, CASEY
GILLIGAN, BROCK
GILLON, ERNEST JOHN
GILMORE, KEVIN
GILMOUR, STEPHEN
GILSON, MARK
GILTRAP, STAN
GING, COLIN
GINI, LUIS
GINNS, REES
GINNS, BRETT
GIOKARIS, PETER
GIOKARIS, NICK
GIRGIS, GEORGE
GJALTEMA, JOHN
GLADWELL, CHRISTOPHER
GLASSIE, TERRY
GLAVAN, DOUG DAMIR
GLENDINNING, DUNCAN
JAMES
GLENNIE, MICHAEL
GOBRIEL, KAMAL
GODFREY, AARON
GODFREY, EUGENE
GODING, DAVID
GOEDEE, SCOTT
GOEDEE, CRAIG JOHN
GOLDBERG, PAUL
GOLDBERT, RONALD
GOLDING, SHAUN
GOLDMAN, GRANT
GOLDSMITH, CRAIG
GOLLAN, DONNY

GOLMAN, SERGE
GOMES, DOMINGOS
GONCALVES, PAULO TORRES
GONCALVES, JOSE MARIS
GONCALVES, JOAO
GONZALE'Z, MANUEL
GONZALES, ROBERTO
GONZALEZ, RAUL
GONZALEZ, WALTER
GONZALEZ, MIGUEL A
GONZALEZ, JOSE
GOOCH, ROBERT
GOOD, TONY
GOODGER, WAYNE
GOODMAN, DAVID
GOODMAN, DAVID
GOODWIN, MICHAEL JOHN
GOODY, MICHAEL
GORALEWSKI, ANDREW
GORDON, REX
GORDON, ANGUS
GORGIZKHAH, LYON
GORICK, GLENN
GORMAN, JAMES
GORMAN, NOEL
GOSKA, STAN
GOSKA, JOSEPH
GOSPOCIC, ZAC
GOSSES, RICK
GOSTEVSKY, STEPHANIE
GOTO, YOSHIYUKI
GOUGH, DANIEL JOHN
GOULD, DALE
GOULDER, MICHAEL
GOURLAY, NIGEL
GOVORCIN, BRIAN
GRACA, ALBERTINO
GRACE, FREDERICK
GRACE, BARRIE WAYNE
GRAHAM, NIGEL
GRAHAM, GARY
GRAHAM, TONY CHARLES
GRAHAM, BOB JOSEPH
GRAINGER, GUY
GRAINGER, ROBERT JOE
GRANA, RAUL
GRANATA, BOB
GRANGER, IAN
GRANT, REX
GRANT, COLIN
GRANT, MICHAEL ALLAN
GRANT, CHRISTOPHER
GRANT, NOEL
GRANT, ALLAN
GRASEVSKI, GORAN
GRASSBERGER, MARC
GRASSI, PAUL
GRASSO, MICHAEL
GRASSO, ANTHONY

GRASSO, SANTO
GRASSO, DANIEL
GRASSO, JOE
GRAUE, MARK
GRAY, DARRYL JOHN
GRAY, PAUL
GRAY, ANDREW
GRAY, JOEL
GRAY, DAVE
GRAZIANO, GIUSEPPE
GREATREX, ROB
GREEN, WARWICK
GREEN, ALLAN
GREEN, RICHARD
GREENTREE, JAMIE JOHN
GREGORY, ADAM
GREGORY, PETER
GREGORY-NAUN], JASON
GREVETT, DOUGLAS
GRIBBLE, MICK
GRIFFEN, RONALD JOSEPH
GRIFFITHS, MIKE
GRIFFITHS, JENNY MAREE
GRIGGS, STEWART
GRIGULL, GERD
GRILO, JOAO
GRIMES, JIM
GRIMSON, RICKY
GROEN, MARTIN
GROGAN, PAUL
GROMOF, ALEX
GRONO, NORMAN
GRUN, DIETER
GRUNDY, DAVID LEE
GUALDI, JOHN
GUERRA, PETER
GUERREIRO, AGUSTINO
GUERRERA, ANGELO
GUERRERA, ANTONO
GUIA, HUMBERTO
GUIDOLIN, ROMANO
GUIMARAES, JONO
GULIH, DINKO
GUNDRY, STEPHEN
GUNDRY, JOHN
GURNEY, WARREN
GURR, PHILLIP
GURR, SHANE
GUTIERREZ, HECTOR
GUY, JOANNE MARION
GWYNNE, DAVID
HAAMI, DAVID
HABIB, VICTOR
HABIB, JOSEPH
HABKOUK, GEORGE
HABRA, MICK
HACKETT, IAN MAURICE
HADARIN, MICHAEL JOHN
HADARIN, ALEXANDER

HADARIN, GREG
HADFIELD, PETER
HADFIELD, PAUL
HADZALIC, NERMIN
HAES, CHRISTOPHER
HAGARTY, TROY
HAGE, RICHARD
HAGEN, BILL
HAKARAIA, MARVIN
HALE, STEVEN
HALFPENNY, ROBERT
HALL, BRIAN
HALL, STUART
HALL, PETER
HALL, TRACY
HALL, DAVID
HALL, DEREK
HALL, STEPHEN
HALL, DANIEL GERARD
HALL, ANDREW
HALLCROFT, STEPHEN
HALLIDAY, PETER
HALLIGAN, SHAY
HAMAM, NADER
HAMBLION, BOB
HAMID, YOUSOFF
HAMILTON, RON
HAMILTON, JASON
HAMMERSLEY, ADAM
HAMMON, CHARLES LESLIE
HAMNETT, NEIL
HAMORI, JOHN
HAMPSEY, PETER MARTIN
HAMPSON, SCOTT ROGER
HAMZA, MARTIN
HAMZA, MARTIN
HAN, SANG KYUN
HAN, CHANG SEOP
HAN, DONG QUIN
HANCOCK, WAYNE
HAND, PETER
HANHAM, MIKE
HANN, KHUNNY
HANNA, IAN
HANNA, DARREN MICHEAL
HANNAFORD, GEORGE
HANNAH, JOHN MICHAEL
HANNAH, PETER
HANNAH, LIAM
HANNAH, EAMONN
HANNAN, BRADLEY JOHN
HANRAHAN, DAVID
HANSEN, PETER
HANSON, MICHAEL
HANZEK, STJEPAN
HARATSARIS, THEO
HARDIE, MARK
HARDING, MICHAEL
HARDING, MICHAEL

HARDMAN, GLEN
HARDY, KENNETH
HARDY, BRENDAN
HARGRAVE, GARRY JOHN
HARGRAVES, NEIL
HARITOS, ANGELO
HARKNESS, DONALD
HARLAND, SCOTT PETER
HARNETT, RICHARD
HARRETT, LARRY
HARRINGTON, GREG
HARRINGTON, DANIEL
HARRINGTON, PAT
HARRIS, COL
HARRIS, MICHAEL
HARRIS, ALEXANDER
HARRIS, NOEL
HARRIS, GREG
HARRIS, KEVIN
HARRIS, GLEN MALCOLM
HARRIS, SOPHIE
HARRIS, PETER
HARRISON, MICHAEL SHANE
HARRISON, SIMON
HARRISON, WYLIE
HARRISON, KEVIN
HARRISON, DALE
HARRISON, MARK PETER
HARRISON, IAN
HART, BRETT STEVEN
HART, MATTHEW
HARTLAND, PAUL
HARTLETT, STEPHEN
HARTLEY, MARK ANDREW
HARTLEY, GARRY
HARTLEY, ROB
HARTMANN, MARK
HARTOUNIAN, EMIL
HARTY, RAYMOND
HARTZENBERG, PIERRE
HARVEY, PETER EDWARD
HARVEY, WAYNE
HARVEY, CHRISTOPHER
HARVEY, BRETT
HARVIE, GLEN
HASKINS, BRADY
HASSE, ROLF
HASTINGS, ANDREW
HATAVA, SAMUEL
HATAVA, JOEL
HATCH, MARK ANTHONY
HATCHER, PETER
HATTON, GEOFFREY
HATTON, GEOFF
HATTON, JASON
HAVEBOND, KEVIN
HAWEA, KARENA
HAWES, WILLIAM
HAWKE, BRETT

HAWKES, JOHN
HAWKES, PHIL
HAWKINS, HOWARD
HAWKINS, PAUL
HAWLI, MOHAMAD
HAWTHORN, LEX
HAY, BILLY
HAYDAY, RUSSELL
HAYES, JAMES
HAYES, PHILLIP
HAYNES, MATTHEW
HAYNES, ROSS
HAYWARD, KENNETH
HAZELDINE, MICKY
HE, GUOXING
HEALY, LIAM DAVID
HEALY, GARVAN JAMES
HEALY, PHILIP
HEAP, GEOFFREY
HEARN, EDWARD ALEXANDER
HEARN, MICK
HEARN, COLIN
HEATHER, JOHN
HEATON, WILLIAM
HEDDLE, STUART
HEDGE, GLENN
HELLAWELL, JOHN
HEMMETT, JUSTIN
HEMMINGS, ANDREW
HENAO, PABLO
HENAO, JUAN
HENARE, PHILLIP
HENAWAY, MICHAEL
HENDERSON, NEIL
HENDERSON, ROB
HENDERSON, PAUL
HENDRY, STEVEN
HENDRY, TERRY
HENESS, SCOTT
HENG, CHRIS
HENLEY, MARK
HENNESSY, THOMAS
HENNESSY, PETER
HENRIKSEN, PER
HENRIQUES, ANTONIO
HENRY, ANGELA
HENRY, PAUL
HENTUNEN, PERTTI ANTERO
HENWOOD, KELLY LOUISE
HEO, BAEK SOOL
HEO, HAN WOOK
HERBERT, IAN
HERBERT, ADRIAN
HERDER, JOHN
HERNANDEZ, RICARDO
HERRERA, SANDRA
HERRY, DENNIS
HERTNER, CHRIS
HESPE, IAIN DONALD

STEWART
HESS, ALAN
HESSION, EUGENE
HESSION, GRANT
HETARAKA, ROBERT
HETMAN, GUY
HETMANSKI, MARK
HEVER, ANTHONY
HEWITT, DARREN JAMES
HEWITT, WILLIAM
HEWITT, GEOFF
HEYDON, STEVE
HGNARE, REWA
HGUYEN, DUY CHINH
HIBBERT, JOHN
HICKEY, CHRISTOPHER
HICKEY, LEE
HICKEY, ANDREW
HICKIE, DAVID
HICKMOTT, GRANT
HICKS, RONALD
HICKS, CHRIS
HICKS, MARK
HICKS, NATHAN
HIGGINS, NIALL BERNARD
HIGGON, DAVE
HIKUROA, KEVIN
HILAN, STEPHEN JOHN
HILL, CHRIS
HILL, ALBERT
HILL, GLENN
HILL, WILLIAM
HILLEN, ANDREW
HILLS, RICHARD
HINCHLIFFE, MARK
HINGAIA, JOHN
HINGAIA, JOHN
HINKLEY, DAVID
HINTE, ERIC JASON
HISING, ADAM
HITCHCOCK, ERIC
HO, THUNG
HOBDAY, JAMES NICHOLAS
HOBOR, ADAM DAVID
HOBOR, JOE
HOBSON, DENNIS
HOCKING, KRIS
HOCROFT, RUSSELL
HODCROFT, SHANE
HODGE, DAVID
HODGES, LUKE
HODGETT, RICHARD JAMES
HODGKINSON, VINCENT
HODZIC, ASIM
HOESTRA, JOE
HOFFMANN, GUENTER
HOGAN, GERARD MICHAEL
HOGAN, PAUL
HOGAN, TONY

HOGG, GORDON
HOKIANGA, FRANK GEORGE
HOLCOMB, LES
HOLD, SHANE
HOLDEN, STEPHEN
HOLDER, GEOFFREY
HOLDER, JAMES
HOLDERNESS, TRACEY
HOLGUIN, FELIX
HOLLEY, JIM
HOLMES, BRIAN
HOLOHAN, SEAN
HOLT, DAVID
HOLT, GARY
HOLT, RICK
HOME, MATT
HONG, MYUNG HWA
HONG, WAN KYUN
HOOK, ADAM
HOOKER, WAYNE
HOOKER, RICHARD KARL
HOOLEY, MICHAEL
HOOPER, GREG
HOPE, MATTHEW
HOPKINSON, FRED
HOPOI, TAURA
HORAN, MARK
HORE, CHARLES
HORN, MARK
HORNHEIM, DIRK
HORON, BRAD
HOROWITZ, LEO
HORSEY, WAYNE
HORWOOD, BRUCE
HOSKING, TREVOR
HOTSON, JAMES
HOUGH, ROBERT
HOUGH, MICHAEL
HOUGHTON, CARL
HOULIARAS, STEVE
HOULLARAS, STEVE
HOURA, TREVOR
HOURA, WHITI [JEFF]
HOURANI, SAMIR
HOVENDEN, DAVID
HOWARD, KIM
HOWARD, GRANT
HOWARD, CRAIG EMMETT
HOWARD, GARY
HOWARTH, CRAIG
HOWARTH, NEVILLE
HOWLE, DAVID
HUANG, RONG DO
HUANG, HOU RONG
HUCKLE, WARNER
HUDSON, JAMES
HUDSON, NATHAN
HUDSON, ROD
HUDSON, PAUL RICHARD

HUERTAS, MAURICIO
HUGGINS, BRETT
HUGGINS, SHANE CAMERON
HUGGINS, LIESA
HUGHES, GAVIN
HUGHES, MAL
HUGHES, COLIN
HUGHES, KERRY
HUGHES, DANNY
HUGHES, CHRIS
HUGHS, TIM
HUME, BRETT
HUMPAGE, PAUL
HUNT, BRIAN STANLEY
HUNT, JOHN
HUNT, PATRICK JOHN
HUNT, DONALD
HUNT, ANTHONY
HUNT, CHRISTOPHER
HUNTRISS, GREG
HURIWAI, ERIN JON
HUSKING, BRIAN
HUTCHINGS, GREGORY
HUTCHINGS, STEVEN
HUTCHINSON, WADE
HUTCHISON, MARTIN
HUTCHISON, IAN
HUTCHISON, DAVID
HUTTLEY, IAN
HUTTON, LEONARD PAUL
HUTTON, JOANNE
HUTTON, SCOTT
HYDE, STEPHEN
HYDE, BEN
HYMANN, MICHAEL
IACULLO, VITO
IANNI, DICK
IBACETA, ANDRES
IBARBURU, NILO
IBBOTSON, PAUL
IENCO, ROBERT
IEROPOLI, NICOLA
IKAMUI, SOANE
ILIC, RADOVAN
ILICH, MICHAEL
IM, YOUNG SUP
IM, MOUNG KI
IMMONEN, EINO
IN HOE, KU
INA, TANAGATA
IND, GRANT ANTHONY
ING, NATH
INGLETON, RYAN
INGLIS, DAVID
INGLIS, GARTH
INGLIS, JETHRO
INGLIS, CLIFF
INGOLD, PAUL
INGRAM, MARK

INIC, JOVICA	JEFFERSON, JOHN	JONES, PATRICK	KARAKOUSIS, BILL	KERANOVIC, ZEHIDA	KING, RAWIRI	KOTEVSKI, ILO	LAING, DAVID
INNES, TRAVIS	JEFFERY, JASON	JONES, JOHN	KARAM, ANTHONY JOSEPH	KEREMETE, ROBERT	KINGI, DAVID NOLAN	KOTZATSIS, ALEX	LALIOTITIS, CHRISTOS
INNS, BRIAN	JEFFERY, MARK	JONES, STEPHEN	KARAN, ZDRAVKO	KERIN, GEOFF	KINGI, JADE	KOULLIAS, MANUEL	LALOR, PETER
INSUA, JULIO	JEFFERYS, JOHN	JONES, NEIL	KARLOVCEC, MARTIN	KERR, LEONARD R H	KIRA, LEONARD R H	KOULLIAS, TONY	LALOR, RICK
INVERARITY, DAVID	JEFFRIES, CHRIS	JONES, GLENN	KARLOVCEC, GEORGE	KERR, STEVE	KIRKLAND, COLLEEN	KOUROUTIS, PETER	LAM, PAULO
IOAKIM, ROSS	JELINIC, IVAN	JONES, DAVID	KARMADONOFF, GEORGE	KERR, CRAIG	KIRKPATRICK, ROBERT	KOVACEVIC, JOHN	LAMB, GRAHAM
IOAN, WAPEU	JENKINS, FRANK	JONES, GLYN	KARWALA, SYLVESTER	KERR, ROY	KIRTON, PAUL	KOVACEVIC, MILE PETER	LAMBERT, CHRIS
IOANNOV, GEORGIOS	JENKINS, GEORGE C	JONES, DAVID	KASIOU, LOUIE	KERRIGAN, COLIN DAVID	KIRWAN, GEOFF	KOVARIK, SAM	LAMOND, COLIN
IOCCA, JOHN ANTHONY	JENKINS, SHAUN	JONES, JAMES	KASSIOTES, EVANGELOS	KERRY, DARYL	KITA, SAAN	KOVIC, PETER	LAMPASONA, CARMELO
IPPOLITI, MICHAEL	JENKINS, TROY	JONES, MARK	KASSIR, RAED	KERSHAW, STEPHEN	KITCHENER, TIM	KOWAL, TARAS	LANDERS, PHIL
IRONS, BRAD	JENNINGS, PAUL	JONES, JAMES	KATALINIC, MARIO	KERVINEN, TIMO JUHANI	KIUELA, GARY ADRIAN	KOZAK, PETER	LANDRIGAN, DAVID
IRVINE, MARTIN VICENT	JENNINGS, GEOFFREY PAUL	JONES, CHRISTOPHER	KATENE, CONWAY	KERVINEN, ILMO	KIUMAN, CHENG	KOZARAC, MUJAGA	LANE, ROBERT JOHN
IRVINE, NATHAN	JEREBICANIN, NEDZAD	JORDAN, JOHN JOE	KATON, JACK	KESKI NUMMI, TIMO	KIVELA, REIJO	KOZARAC, SENADA	LANE, OWEN
IRVINE, NEIL	JERMEN, MARIO	JORGENSEN, DAVID	KATSENOS, JIMIS	KEUR, JASON	KLAMER, DENIS	KOZOMARA, MLADEN	LANE, ADAM
IRWIN, ALAN	JESSIMAN, GARRY	JOSEPH, ROBERT	KAUHIVA, TONY	KEW, MARK ALAN	KLEASE, DAVID	KRAEFT, KARL	LANE, MATT
IRWIN, DAVID	JESSUP, DAVID	JOSHI, BHARATKUMAR	KAUI, MALCOLM THOMAS	KHADEM, MICK	KLEINDIENST, JOHN A	KRAHMALOV, JORGE	LANGE, GARRY
IRWIN, CRAIG	JEVTIC, MLADEN	JOURDAIN, STEPHEN	KAVANAGH, MICHAEL	KHALIFE, ANTHONY	KLEM, MARK	KRENN, ANDREW	LANGFORD, MICHAEL
IRWIN, LUKE	JEWELL, RUSSELL	DOUGLAS	KAVANAGH, PETER	KHAMIS, YUSUF	KLITSIDIS, CON	KRKLJES, ZDRAVKO	LANGFORD, JEFFREY
ISAACS, ANDREW	JIANG, XUE SONG	JOYCE, SEAN	KAY, BILL	KHAN, MICHAEL	KLJAIC, MARKO	KRKLJES, MILOS	LANGLEY, MICHAEL
ISGRO, ANTONINO	JIMENEZ, CESAR	JUAREZ, EDUARDO DANIEL	KEATING, EOIN	KHAN, MOHAMMED	KLJAIC, BOZO	KRPAN, ZIGGI	LANGRIDGE, STEPHEN
ISHERWOOD, CHRIS	JIN, CHAN SHAN	JUAREZ, ALVARO	KEAVENEY, JIM	KHEM, THIN	KLJAJIC, BORO	KRSTIC, STEVAN	LANIGAN, PETER FRANCIS
ISSA, YOUSSEF	JIN, ALEXEY	JUBB, DARRYL JAMES	KEEBLE, STUART	KHODER, MICHAEL	KLOBAS, RIKO	KUEGERL, FRANK	LANNOY, ANTHONY
ITTENSOHN, DAVID	JIN, XIAN	JUCHEWICZ, ANTONIO	KEEGAN, DAVID	KHOU, CHHAY	KLOBUCAR, STEPHEN	KUHLMANN, MICK	LAPI, SEBASTIAN
IVANISEVIC, ZLATKO	JOHANSEN, BENT	JUDD, ALAN MARK	KEELING, BRETT	KHOU, KHOA	KNAPPETT, RICHARD JOHN	KUKAVICA, MARKO	LAPIC, MICHAEL
IVANOVIC, VELJKO	JOHANSON, RUSSELL	JUN, TAE-KWON	KEEN, ROBERT	KHOU, MENG	KNELLER?, ALLAN	KULK, JON	LAPIENIS, EDDI
IVELJA, LAWRENCE	LYNDON	JUNG, YOUNG-BOK	KEITH, JOHN	KHOURY, CHRISTOPHER	KNEZEVIC, DALIBOR	KULMER, GERHARD	LARKIN, ANDREW
IVES, GREGORY PAUL	JOHNS, ROGER	JUNQ, CHOONG SIK	KELAHER, SUSAN GAY	KIDD, IAN	KNIGHT, RICHARD	KUMAR, RAJEND	LARMER, PHILLIP
IVSAN, PAUL	JOHNSON, CHRISTOPHER	JURGENS, IAN DAVID	KELETT, LEIGH	KILBY, BRETT	KNIGHT, ROBIN JACK	KUMAR, KISHORE	LARSEN, STEPHEN
IVSAN, ADAM	JOHNSON, WAYNE	JURMAN, MAURO	KELLIE, TOM	KILFEATHER, ALISTAIR HUGH	KNIGHT, PAUL ANTHONY	KUNISS, PETER	LARSEN, ANDREW
IVSIC, TONY	JOHNSON, DANIEL	JURY, NICHOLAS	KELLS, JASON	KILIAN, DAVID IAN	KNIGHT, DAVE	KURBAJ, NIDAL	LASORSA, NICK
JACKS, TANE	JOHNSON, TIMOTHY	JURY, ANDREW	KELLY, DAVID	KILIBARDA, ZORAN	KNIGHT, JOHN	KURESA, CHRIS	LASOVSKI, TONY
JACKSON, GLYN	JOHNSON, TREVOR	JURY, RUSSELL DESMOND	KELLY, CHARLEY	KILPATRICK, JAMES	KNIGHT, DAX	KURJAKOVIC, ANTON	LASPATZIS, NICK
JACKSON, IAN	JOHNSON, TIM	KADER, ABDUL	KELLY, STEVEN	KIM, YEOM SAM	KNIGHT, ERROL JAMES	KURTIAK, JOHN	LATCHAM, MARK
JACKSON, WAYNE	JOHNSON, JOSEPH	KADIC, DJEMAL	KELLY, PHILIP	KIM, JEA HONG	KNIGHT, JAI COLIN	KURU, CLEVELAND	LATIMER, WILLIAM
JACKSON, MICHAEL	JOHNSON, COLIN	KAFATARIS, JIM	KELLY, PAUL	KIM, HEE SAM	KNIGHT, DESMOND JOSEPH	KUSTRO, KARLO	LATIMER, NICK JOHN
JACOB, GEORGE	JOHNSON, STEPHEN EDWARD	KAHUKIWA, JASON	KELLY, JIM	KIM, MIHG SHAN	KNIGHTS, ASHLEY	KUVENER, FRANS	LAUGHTON, JUSTIN
JACOB, BYRON	JOHNSON, LEE PATRICIA	KAIPO, WILLY	KELLY, DAVID PATRICK	KIM, KI-HO	KNIGHTS, MATTHEW	KUYL, JOHN	LAUGHTON, DALLAS
JACOBS, BRIAN	JOHNSON, DARREN	KAISSER, NICK [BEEFA]	KELLY, JAMES	KIM, YOON-SAM	KNOTEK, DANIEL	KWAN, KEVIN	LAURENCE-ROGERS, DANIEL
JAE JUN, KIM	JOHNSON, JOHN	KALETH, ANDREW	KELLY, ROGER	KIM, TAE HYUNG	KNOWLAND, PETER	KWAN, JEREMY	LAURIE, KEITH
JAFFAR, HUSSEIN	JOHNSON, STEVEN	KALI, CELIL	KELSON, GARY	KIM, KI TAE	KNOX, PAUL	KWAN, JULIAN	LAVETTE, MARK
JAGLIC, VLADIMIR	JOHNSTON, WATTIE ALEX	KALINA, MATE	KEMAL, HASSAN	KIM, BYUNG HYUNG	KNOX, FRED	KWANG PIL, KIM	LAW, BEN
JAGLIC, STANKO	JOHNSTON, COLIN GEOFFREY	KALLIS, KEITH	KENDELL, DARRELL	KIM, YOUNG SAM	KOBERSY, FADI	KYD, KEVIN	LAWLOR, MATTHEW
JAKSIC, MILAN	JOHNSTON, BRIAN	KAMBEROVIC, SEAD	KENNEDY, DAVID NEIL	KIM, SANG CHUL	KOCIC, SENAD	KYD, MARCEL	LAWRENCE, STEPHEN
JAMES, GARETH	JOHNSTON, TOMMY JOE	KAMBOUROGLOU, MICHAEL	KENNEDY, GARRY	KIM, YOUNG MIN	KOCIC, NEDZAD	KYPREOS, NICK	LAWRENCE, IAN
JAMES, KENNETH	JOHNSTON, MARK	KANAZIR, BOGDAN	KENNEDY, FINN	KIMANI, KENNEDY MINANGI	KOCIC, OSMAN	KYRIACOU, JIM	LAWRENCE, DARREN
JAMES, DAVID	JOKIC, RADOVAU	KANE, CORNELL	KENNEDY, PHILLIP	KING, KEVIN JAMES	KOFLER, HANS	LA LOGGIA, ANGELA	LAWRENCE, PETER JOHN
JAMES, CHARLES	JOKIC, DAVOR	KANE, EVAN	KENNEDY, TERRY	KING, NEIL	KOKAUA, ARAMAMAO	LA MONICA, SANTO	LAWRENCE, CLIVE
JAMES, JOHN	JOKIC, VELIMIR	KANG, CHANG HWAN	KENNEDY, CLAYTON	KING, DARYL JOHN	KOKIRI, MICHAEL	LABA, ZIGGY	LAWRENCE, PETER
JAMES, TREVOR	JOLLY, THOMAS	KANG, SUK PYO	KENNEDY, BRIAN	KING, TREVOR	KOLC, LUKE	LABRA, EUGENIA	LAWRY, ANTHONY
JAMES, GLENN	JONES, JASON WAYNE	KANG, YEON-HI	KENNEDY, LEIGH	KING, ERNIE	KOLTSIS, ARI	LACEY, RICHARD	LAWSON, STEWART
JAMESON, TERRY	JONES, MICHAEL	KAPAC, DAVOR	KENNEY, MICHAEL	KING, BRENDON PAUL	KONG, NARITH	LACY, PETER THOMAS	LAWSON, JAMES EDWARD
JANG, MYUNG OK	JONES, COLIN B	KAPELLOS, SAM	KENNY, SCOTT	KING, ADAM	KOPA, TERRY	LAFITANI, OUENI	LAWSON, JUSTIN
JANKIEWICZ, JIM	JONES, PETER	KAPITANOF, ATHANASIOS	KENT, NEVILLE	KING, ANDREW	KOPPMAN, BARRY	LAGO, JUAN CARLOS	LAWSON, BRENT
JANSE, ANDREW JOHN	JONES, DAVID	KAPITANOVIC, ZORAN	KENT, MICHAEL DENNIS	KING, JASON	KORBULA, GEORGE	LAGOPOULOS, MICHAEL	LAWSON, LARRY CHARLES
JARMAN, MICHAEL	JONES, ROBERT G	KAPUR, EDIB	KENYON, CRAIG	KING, DONALD	KOSIAK, ALEX	LAGUDI, MICK	LAYCOCK, COLIN
JARQUIN, RAU'L	JONES, CLINTON	KAPUR, SALEM	KEOGH, PATRICK	KING, KEN	KOSORUKOW, SCOTT	LAGUDI, MICK	LAYTON, PAUL
JARRETT, KEN	JONES, DESMOND	KAPUR, ELMEDIH	KEPPEL, DION MICHAEL	KING, JASON LOW MENG	KOSTOPOULOS, STEVEN	LAGUZZA, JOHN	LAZARUS, JAY
JAWORSKI, EDMUND STEFAN	JONES, ALAN	KARACIANNIS, CHRIS	KEPPEL, AMANDA	KING, ANDREW	KOSTURA, BORIS	LAHIFF, PHILLIP JAMES	LE BRETON, MATTHEW
JAY, CHRISTOPHER	JONES, BRIAN	KARADIMITROS, THEO	KEPPEL, MICHAEL	KING, ALAN RONALD	KOT, ADAM	LAIDLAW, SCOTT	LE BUSQUE, STUART HARRY

LEA, PETER
LEA, DAVID RAYMOND
LEAUDAIS, GEOFF
LECKEY, DARREN
LECLERC, DEAN
LEDINGHAM, DONALD
LEE, ELLY
LEE, AARON GRAY
LEE, JOHN
LEE, PAUL
LEE, DAE SUK
LEE, SEI WOON
LEE, RON
LEE, RICHARD
LEE, SANG BAK
LEE, PAUL
LEE, SANG HAK
LEE, KYUM YOUNG
LEE, CHANG MO
LEE, DONG NO
LEE, EDDIE
LEE, KYU - YEAL
LEE, BONG KEUN
LEE, SOO CHEOL
LEE, JONG-SUK
LEE, HO SEOK
LEE, FEEHAN
LEESON, DAVID
LEGER, ALLY
LEGGETT, GREG
LEHNER, ANDREW
LEHTO, JEFFERY
LEIGH, ADAM
LEMARSENY, ADAM
LEMOS, RICHARD DANIEL
LENGYEL, CHRISTIAN
LENIHAN, MICHAEL
LENNON, MALCOLM
LENNON, ROD
LENNOX, LUKE
LENNOX, ROBERT
LENTFER, PAUL
LEO, ALLAN MICHAEL
LEO, GARY
LEONARD, CAMERON
LEONG MUN, WILLIAM
LEPORE, VITO
LEQUESNE, GREG
LESNIK, IVAN
LESUEUR, NOLAN
LETOGA, TREVOR JOSEPH
LEVER, TREVOR
LEWIS, RONALD
LEWIS, KEVIN
LEWIS, COLIN
LEWIS, MARK ROBERT
LI, SHI MING
LI, LIAN SUO
LIAKOS, STEVE

LIBRERI, STEVEN
LIBRERI, STEVEN
LIGHTBODY, NORMAN
LIHB, KARIM
LIIBUS, PETER
LILLIA, WAYNE
LILLIA, STEVE
LIM, YOUNG IL
LIN, JOHN
LIN, DAVID
LIN, HUI ZENG
LINDORES, KEVIN
LINDSAY, WALTER
LINDSAY, STUART
LINDSELL, JEREME
LINDSEY, JOHN
LINDSTROM, TIM
LINES, JACQUELINE
LINNENBANK, HENDRIKUS C
LINNETT, MICHAEL JOHN
LINO, CANDIDO
LINTOTT, GARY
LIOTTA, FRANK
LIPARI, ANTONIO
LIPOVAC, TONY
LIRAS, NICOLOAS
LISBOA, ADALMO
LISSING, JERRY
LITSTER, GRANT
LITTLE, WARREN
LIVINGSTONE, DAVID
LLOYD, MORGAN
LLOYD, CRAIG
LLOYD, ANDREW
LO GIUDICE, MARIO
LOCHHEAD, ALEX
LOCHMANN, MICHAEL
LOCKHORST, VICTOR JOHN
LOCKWOOD, KEVIN
LOCKWOOD, MARK JASON
LOCKYER, STEPHEN JOHN
LOENEN, DAVID
LOGAN, GRAEME FRANCIS
LOGUE, STEPHEN
LOIACONO, STEVEN ANTHONY
LOIACONO, MARIO
LOKA, FOAD
LOLESIO, PETER
LONERGAN, MICHAEL
LONG, GORDON
LONGO, ENZO
LOPES, JOSE
LOPES, AFONSO JOSE
LOPEZ, RAYMOND
LOPEZ, JULIO
LOPEZ, ELISEO
LOPEZ, ALICIA
LOPEZ, MANUEL

LOSURDO, ANTONIO
LOSURDO, JOSEPH
LOUANGAMATH, YOUTHANET
LOUGHNAN, JOHN
LOUK, SAM NANG
LOURENCO, ANTONIO
LOVELL, STEPHEN
LOVERIDGE, JAMIE
LOVETT, PETER ALAN
LOVIC, HILMIJA
LOWE, CHRISTOPHER
LOWE, ROBERT
LOWE, CHRISTOPHER
LU, XIANG WEI
LU, GEORGE
LUBACH, WAYNE
LUCACI, MARK JOHN
LUCAS/OTIS, JOHN
LUCISANO, MELISA
LUCKMAN, DAVID
LUCOCK, ROSS
LUCY, JAMES
LUCZKA, RUSSELL
LUKANOVIC, IVICA
LUKEZIC, KARL ANTON
LUNN, SYMON
LUONG, VINH QUOC HUNG
LUONGO, JOSEPH
LUOTI, VOITTO
LUTHER, CRAIG
LY, VINCENT
LYALL, GREG ROSS
LYE, STEPHEN
LYKOUREZOS, CHRIS
LYNCH, JOHN
LYNCH, STEPHEN
LYNCH, DOMINIC
LYNCH, SIMON
LYNE, GARETH
LYNN, RUPERT
MAC GREGOR, ROBERT
MACBRIDE, RICHARD MARK A.
MACCARONE, SAM
MACCHION, LAMBERT
MACDONALD, BRETT JOHN
MACDONALD, BRUCE
MACDONALD, ANDREW
MACHADO, JOAQUIM
MACHIN, ABEL
MACK, ALLAN
MACKAY, JAMES
MACKAY, SCOTT
MACKAY, ALISTAIR
MACKENZIE, JAMES ROSS
MACKENZIE, ANDREW ROBERT
MACKENZIE, JOANNA LOUISE
MACKEY, BRENDAN
MACLAREN, SELENA

MACLEAN, MARK
MACLEOD, NEIL
MACNAUGHTON, GARY
MACPHERSON, THOMAS
MACTAVISH, ALAN
MADDEN, ROBERT
MADDOCK, ANDREW
MADRID, JULIO
MAFFI, ARTHUR
MAGEE, LAWRENCE
MAGLIS, JOHN
MAGNOCAVALLO, MARIO
MAGNOCAVALLO, MARK
MAGNUSSON, THOR
MAGRI, ROBERT
MAGRIN, JOHN PETER
MAHE, PAUL
MAHER, CHRIS
MAHONEY, ROBBIE
MAHONEY, JOUSHUA
MAHONY, RICHARD
MAHLENHOFF, WOLFGANG
MAHOJLOVIC, DURO GEORGE
MARIC, TOMISLAN
MAIJALA, MATTI HENRIKKI
MAJSTOROVIC, IVICA PERE
MAKAPELU, JUNIOR
MAKAROFF, VICTOR
MAKIN, PETER
MAKIN, ANTHONY JOHN
MAKINGS, NEIL
MAKSIMOVIC, GORAN
MALDONADO, ESTEBAN
MALEK, SAMUEL JOHN
MALEK, EDWARD
MALEN, PERTTI ANTERO
MALIC, JOE
MALICIA, HENRIQUE
MALINIC, RADE
MALINOVIC, NEDELJKO
MALLO, PABLO
MALONE, BRENDAN
MALONE, ANDREW
MALVERN, GEORGE
MAMO, WAYNE
MANAPORI, TEKAVENGA
MANDIC, DAVID
MANGA, SHANE MICHEAL
MANGAN, SCOTT
MANGOLD, DOUGLAS
MANIATIS, ANTHONY
MANLEY, TERENCE
MANLEY, IAN
MANN, DAVID
MANN, RICHARD
MANNALL, MATTHEW
MANNERS, SIMON
MANNING, SHANE
MANNING, MICHAEL
MANNINO, DANIEL

MANOJLOVIC, DUSAN
MANOJLOVIC, DURO
MANUEL, ANTHONY
MANUEL, TONY
MANUEL, EDWARD JOSEPH
MANUKAU, DAVID
MANUKAU, AARON
MANUKONGA, JOHN
MANUKONGA, JAMIE NATHAN
MANZOOR, HUSSAIN
MARCH, JOHN
MARCH, JOHN
MARCHESE, ROBERT
MARCHIG, ADAM
MARCINA, NENAD
MARCUS, BRUCE
MARCUT, GIOVANNII
MARFELL, WAYNE KERRY
MARGIN, KRISTIAN
MARIC, TOMISLAN
MARIC, IVAN JOSIO
MARICIC, ZORAN
MARIJANOVIC, MLADEN
MARINOS, MAMMY
MARINOS, MANUEL
MARJANAC, MILOSAV
MARKAKIS, JIM
MARKATOS, DENIS
MARKOFF, TONY
MARKOPOULOS, BILL
MARKOPOULOS, ARTHUR
MARKOPOULOS, ANGELO
MARKOPOULOS, ACHILLEAS
MARKOPOULOS, ANDREW
MARKOTA, BRANKO
MARKOTIC, MARINKO
MARKOTIC, RATKO (RAY)
MARKOUSKI, LUBE
MARKOVIC, NIKO
MARKOVIC, GORAN
MARLES, BROOKE
MARNIES, KEITH
MAROTTA, ROBERT
MAROUN, ROBERT
MARQUES, ARCINDO
MARQUES, MANUEL
MARRAS, STEVEN
MARSDEN, TONY
MARSDEN, TONY
MARSH, ROBERT
MARSH, DANIEL
MARSHALL, WAYNE
MARSHALL, RUSSELL
MARSHALL, DARREN JAMES
MARSHALL, KEN
MARSHALL, RODNEY JOHN
MARSHALL, DARREN
MARSLAND, HOWARD
MARSTAELLER, STEPHEN

MARTENS, PAUL
MARTIN, GARY
MARTIN, WILLIAM
MARTIN, JOE JOSEPH
MARTIN, NICHOLAS
MARTIN, PHILLIP
MARTIN, PHILIP
MARTIN, TONY
MARTIN, AARON
MARTIN, JOSE
MARTIN, DAVID JOHN
MARTINELLA, DAMIEN
MARTINEZ, JOHN CHARLES
MARTINOVSKY, VIC
MARTINS, MARIO FERREIRA
MARTINS, MARIO
MARTINS, JOSE
MASON, TIM
MASON, ANDREW
MASON, LAURIE
MASON, SHANE
MASON, SHAREEF
MASSAROTTI, ANTHONY
MASSIH, FRED
MASTERS, CRAIG
MASTROFILIPPO, DOMENICO
MASTROPEROS, MICHAEL
MATAI, NOOAPII
MATAIA, MARK
MATAVESI, KOFEINU
MATHER, MATHEW KEITH
MATHERS, JOHN
MATHESON, STEPHEN
MATHEWS, ANTONY
MATIC, ZORAN
MATIC, MLADEN (MAL)
MATIC, NIKOLA
MATIC, ILIJA
MATINOS, SAM
MATTANI, DON
MATTHEW, FLOYD
MATTHEWS, KIRK
MATTHEWS, KEVIN
MATTHEWS, WILLIAM DANIEL
MATTHEWS, STAR
MATTHEWS, AARON
MATTHEWS, DENNIS
MATVEEV, GENADY
MAURAKIS, JOHN
MAUU, PAULO
MAVIGLIA, BRUNO
MAVIGLIA, JOSEPH
MAVRINAC, STAN
MAVROGIANIS, LOUIS
MAVROGIANNIS, TERRY
MAWSON, TROY
MAY, GRANT RAYMOND
MAY, SIMON
MAYER, LEO

MAYES, DAVID GRAHAM
MAYNE, SCOTT TRENT
MAZZAFERRO, GIUSEPPE
MAZZARA, CORRADO
MAZZAROLO, ANTONIO
MAZZAROLO, LOUIE
MAZZONE, PINO
MC ALLISTER, GRAHAM
MC CALMAN, DARREN
MC CARTHY, TERRY
MC CORMACK, RICHARD
MC DONALD, NATHAN
MC DOUGALL, ROBERT
MC ENNALLY, SHANE
MC KEE, PETER
MC LENNAN, ANDREW
MC MAHON, ROBERT JOSEPH
MC MANUS, PETER
MC NAMARA, PATRICK
MC PARLAND, KEITH
MCALEES, BRIAN
MCALISTER, MARK
MCALLISTER, RAUIRI
MCANULTY, MARK
MCARTHUR, GEOFF
MCAULEY, JAMES
MCBRIDE, KERRY
MCBRIDE, JASON
MCBRIDE, ALEXANDER
MCBRIDE, GERALD
MCBRIDE, ALLEN
MCCALL, JONATHAN
MCCANN, MARTIN
MCCANN, MICHAEL
MCCANN, VINCENT JOHN
MCCANN, ROBERT
MCCARTHY, RONAN
MCCARTHY, BRIAN
MCCARTHY, GARY ALICK
MCCARTNEY, DAVID
MCCLORY, JAMES JOHN
MCCLOSKEY, JOHN
MCCLOSKEY, BOSCO
MCCONKEY, DENNIS
MCCORMACK, MATTHEW
MCCREA, MICHAEL
MCCREADIE, JAMES
MCCULLAGH, JOSEPH
MCCUSKEY, CEL
MCDONALD, JOHN
MCDONALD, SHANE
MCDONALD, TRAVIS
MCDONALD, WARWICK
MCDONALD, MATTHEW
MCDONALD, BRETT
MCDONALD, JOHN-PAUL
MCDOUGAL, GRANT
MCDOWALL, JOHN
MCELDOWNEY, JAMES PAUL

MCEVOY, RAY
MCGAHON, PETER
MCGANN, MARK
MCGARRITY, RAY
MCGARRITY, RONALD ARTHUR
MCGARRY, ANTHONY
MCGAULLEY, JACOB
MCGHIE, COLIN
MCGIRR, THOMAS MARTIN
MCGLASHAN, HAMISH
MCGLYNN, CHRIS
MCGOLDRICK, MARK
MCGOLDRICK, CIARAN
MCGOWAN, BARRY SCOTT
MCGOWAN, KENNETH
MCGOWEN, DAVID
MCGRADY, JULIAN
MCGRANAHAN, DAMON
MCGRATH, MICHAEL
MCGRATH, PHILIP
MCGREEVY, MARKIN P
MCGREGER, ROBERT
MCGREGOR, RANALD
MCGREGOR, ADRIAN
MCGRODER, STUART
MCGRORY, TONY
MCGUIGGAN, NICHOLAS
MCHALE, SEAN PATRICK
MCHATTON, KIERAN JAMES
MCHUGH, ANDREW
MCHUGH, JOHN
MCHUGH, ROBERT
MCILHUTTON, DENNIS QUINN
MCINALLY, MATHEW
MCINERNEY, RODNEY
MCINNES, STEPHEN
MCINNES, MICHELLE
MCIVOR, FRANK
MCKAY, PAUL MURRAY
MCKAY, RUSSELL MILLER
MCKENNA, SEAMUS
MCKENZIE, PHILIP
MCKEON, ALLAN SYDNEY
MCKIERNAN, CHARLES
MCKINNON, PETER
MCKINNON, ROBERT
MCKINNON, IAN
MCLAY, NEIL
MCLEAD, CRAIG
MCLEAN, DON
MCLEAN, ROBERT
MCLEAN, JEFFREY
MCLEAN, ROSS
MCLEAN, PHILL
MCLEAN, DARRELL
MCLOUGHLIN, PATRICK
MCMAHON, PETER

MCMAHON, CRAIG
MCMANUS, COLIN
MCMEEL, FINBARR JOHN
MCMILLAN, JASON
MCMILLAN, LUKE
MCMINIMEE, DAVID
MCMURRAY, BEN
MCNAMARA, TONY
MCNICOL, ROBERT LESLIE
MCNULTY, ALAN
MCPHERSON, PHILLIP JOHN
MCPHERSON, BRUCE
MCPHERSON, GLENN
MCPHERSON, PETER
MCQUEEN, STUART
MCQUEEN, COLIN
MCQUEENEY, STEPHEN
MCQUILLAN, TROY
MCRAE, DANIEL
MCSORLEY, BERNARD
MCTAGGART, GREG
MCCULLAGH, MARK
MCWHINNEY, BOB
MEADES, DICK
MEADLEY, GRANT
MEADLEY, TONY
MEADOWS, STACEY
MEAFOU, MATTI
MEAGHER, ANTHONY
MEARING, MARC
MEDAK, MLADEN
MEDBURY, BRYAN DAVID
MEDHURST, BARRY ALLEN
MEEHAN, JOAN
MEHIELOFF, GAVIN
MEHMEDOVIC, SENADA
MEIER, BRIAN
MEIZER, KEVIN
MELE, FULVIO
MELEADY, MARTIN
MELEV, GIOVANNI
MELFI, GIOVANNI
MELILLO, NICK
MELINZ, TIM
MELINZ, JOSH
MELKI, PAUL
MELLUSO, FAUSTO
MELLUSO, FRANCO
MELLUSO, CHARLIE
MELNIKOFF, ALEXANDER
MELQUOT, SARKIS
MELROSE, GREGG
MENDES, DOMINGOS
MENDHAM, JOHN
MENDOZA, ORLANDO
MENTA, ANTONINO
MEPHAM, ROBERT HENRY
MERLETTO, LUIGI
MERONI, STEVE

MERRUTIA, TERRY
MERVIN, LARRY
MESITI, JOHN ADRIAN
METI, JOHN
METLENKO, DANIEL
MEYER, RON
MEZNARIC, ROBERT
MIDSON, BARRY
MIDSON, JAMIE
MIGLIORINO, ROBERT
MIHAIL, TUNTEV
MIHAYLOVIC, GORAN
MIKLAS, MARK
MILAZZO, TORE
MILAZZO, PETER
MILAZZO, VINCENZO
MILDE, ROBERT
MILES, PAUL
MILETIC, BOB
MILETIC, SAM
MILEVSKI, SLAVE
MILGREW, MURRAY
MILILLO, GIUSEPPE (JOE)
MILIOTIS, PETER
MILIS, JOHN
MILJAK, ANTE
MILJAK, DANKO
MILJEVIC, DAVID
MILLAR, PAULA
MILLAR, ARCHIBALD B
MILLBURN, PHIL
MILLER, GREG
MILLER, DEAN
MILLER, JOHN PAUL
MILLER, SHANE
MILLER, PAUL ANTHONY
MILLER, WARREN
MILLER, DOUGLAS
MILLER, ADRIAN
MILLS, COLIN
MILLS, ASHLEY
MILLS, PETER
MILNE, DAVID JAMES
MILOS, MARJANOVIC
MILOSAVLJEVIC, DRAGAN
MILOSTIC, MICHAEL
MILOVAN, CUPAC
MILOVIC, MICK
MILTIADOUS, ELEFTHERIOS
MILTON, LINDSAY THOMAS
MINGAY, JONATHON
MIRARCHI, VINCE
MIRCO, DRASCOVIA
MIRIC, MILAN
MIRIC, MILENKO
MIRIGLIANI, MICHAEL
MIRKOVIC, DUSAN
MITCHELL, JOHN
MITCHELL, ANDREW JAMES

MITCHELL, DARREN
MITCHELL, TONY
MITEK, EVA
MITREVSKI, BRANKO
MITROVIC, BOZO
MITTELHEUSER, GRAHAM
MITTEN, LEANNE
MIYAKAWA, TATSUYA
MOANANU, MAUSALI
MOBBERLEY, DAVID
MOBBS, BRIAN LYALL
MOCKFORD, MARTIN P
MODELLINO, AMEDEO
MODELLINO, PETER
MODINI, JOHN
MOFFATT, JEFFERY
MOFFATT, GUY
MOFFATT, TREVOR
MOFFATT, BEN
MOFFITT, STEPHEN
MOFFITT, GAVIN
MOGHRABI, AMIN
MOHAMAD, ABDUL-LATIF
MOHAMMAD, KAMAL
MOIO, PIERRE
MOISA, PILIPPE EUGENE
MOLLISON, DAVID
MOMCILO, DRACA
MOMI, JOHN
MONAGHAN, PAUL
MONAGHAN, THOMAS
MONK, STEVEN DEREK
MONSIEGNEUR, DARREN CHARLES
MONTES, SERGIO
MONTI, PETER
MOODIE, JOEL
MOODIE, BEN JAMES
MOODY, TODD
MOON, WILLIAM
MOON, TAI-SIK
MOON, POONGSIK
MOON, HONG JANG
MOON, DARREN
MOORE, DECLAN MARTIN
MOORE, DEAN
MOORE, DAVID ELLIOTT
MOORE, CLIFF
MOORE, RAYMOND
MOORE, BRAD
MORALES, CARLOS
MORALES, WASHINGTON
MORALES, ENRIQUE
MORAN, JOHN
MORAN, JAMES
MORENO, ANITA
MORETTI, ROBERTO
MORGAN, JOHN
MORGAN, PETER

MORGAN, RAYMOND
MORGAN, DEAN
MORGAN, KIM
MORGAN, PETER
MORGAN-MONK, CHRISTOPHER
MORIARTY, PAT
MORIN, MICHAEL
MORLEY, STEPHEN
MORRIS, DANNY
MORRIS, MARK WILLIAM
MORRIS, HAROLD
MORRIS, KAYNE
MORRIS, JOHN
MORRISON, DANIEL MARCUS
MORRISON, JAMES
MORRISSEY, PETER
MORSON, PETER
MORTIMER, GLENN
MOSCATIELLO, NICK
MOSES, GEORGE SHANNON
MOSS, NICK
MOSTERT, GAVIN
MOTISI, PAUL
MOTISI, FRANCESCO
MOTTRAM, PAUL
MOTTRAM, BRIAN
MOUBAYED, MOHAMAD
MOUKHAYBER, SALAH
MOULATSIOTIS, CHRISTOS
MOURA, JOSE
MOUSSA, CHARLIE
MOUSSA, RONNY
MOUSSA, MOHAMAD
MOUTEVELIS, ARCHIE
MOUTHAAN, RAYMOND
MOYLAN, TIMOTHY
MOYON, SCOTT
MRAVUNAC, STEVE
MRKIC, MARIO
MUELLER, MARTIN
MUELLER, GERALD
MUHIN, VALERA
MUHIN, PAUL
MUJANOVIC, ZUMRA
MUJANOVIC, IBRAHIM
MULDOON, BRENDAN
MULLAN, AMOS
MULLANE, LIAM
MULVEY, LUKE
MUNCE, COLIN
MUNDO, JOHN
MUNOZ, IGOR
MUNRO, RUSSELL
MURAAHI, MARK
MURDEN, BRETT ANDREW
MURDEN, GRAEME GEORGE
MURDOCH, JOHN
MURPHY, LIAM

MURPHY, JOHN
MURPHY, PETER
MURPHY, TIMOTHY JOHN
MURPHY, CRAIG
MURPHY, DANIEL
MURPHY, EMMETT
MURPHY, STEPHEN
MURPHY, DAN
MURPHY, DANIEL
MURPHY, MICHAEL JAMES
MURPHY, RON
MURRAY, ROBERT WILLIAM
MURRAY, BARRY
MURRAY, VICTOR
MURRAY, RAY
MURRAY, MARK
MUSCATELLO, CARLO
MUSICO, ROCCO
MUSSAP, LEO
MUSSON, SCOTT RICHARD
MUSTAFA, FORTO
MUSTONEN, TONY
MUSUMECI, PAUL
MUSUMECI, ROCCO
MUSUMECI, VINCENT
MUTTON, JAMES
MWINYI, ABDUL
MYLES, GLEN
NACHAR, ROUMANOS
NADEN, STEPHEN
NADIEN, RUSSELL
NAERA, TIM RAWIRI
NAERA, LEONARD
NAGLE, LIAM
NAHLOUS, NASSER
NAHLOUS, HASSAN
NAHLOUS, KHALED
NAHLOUS, MAHMOUD
NAIDOO, DEVEN
NALDER, GARY WARREN
NALDER, MARK
NANCARROW, PETER
NANCARROW, JOHN LESLIE
NAPOLI, CATALDO
NAPOLI, MARTINO
NAPPER, PAUL
NASH, BRIAN
NASH, TENNILLE
NASR, LEE
NASSEREDDINE, MARK
NATTINEN, RAINO VILJO
NAUGHTON, PAUL
NAUGHTON, COLM
NAVENDRA, VIS
NAYLON, LAWSON STUART
NAYLOR, STUART
NDONGA, MOHD
NEALE, DAVID
NECULMAN, FREDDY

NECULMAN, DANIEL
NECULMAN, MARIA
NECULMAN, PEDRO
NECULMAN, WILLIAM
NEE, SHAYNE
NEEVES, JOHN
NEILD, DONALD WILLIAM
NEILSEN, JOHN
NEILSEN, JOHN FREDERICK
NELSON, MICHAEL
NELSON, CRAIG
NESTOROVIC, TOMISLAV
NETHERY, LAWRENCE
NETTLE, JOHN LESLEY
NETTLE, DAVID JOHN
NEUMANN, GARY
NEUMANN, RUSSELL
NEVATTE, DEREK
NEVILLE, BRUCE
NEWBERY, BENJAMIN
NEWMAN, MARK
NEWMAN, CHRIS
NEWTON, ROBERT
NEY, PETER MICHAEL
NG, HIU MAN
NGATAI, RICHARD
NGATI, REON BILLY-JOE
NGO, TU CHIEU
NGUYEN, VAN THUC
NGUYEN, TAN TRUYEN
NGUYEN, NGOC KHIEM
NICHOLAS, RONALD
NICHOLAS, STEWART
NICHOLL, JAMIE
NICHOLSON, JACQUELINE
NICHOLSON, MAURICE
NICHOLSON, TROY
NICHOLSON, KRIS
NICOL, JOSEPH
NICOLITIS, BILL
NIGL, KARL-HEINZ
NIKAC, MILOVOJE
NIKOLAKAKIS, KON
NIKOLIC, PETAR
NIKOLOPOULOS, DANNY
NIKOTIN, PAUL
NILSSON, LARS IVE
NINNES, JOHN
NINNESS, GORDON
NISAN, ALI
NIX, ROBERT
NIXON, ALBERT
NIXON, TOBY
NOBLE, KEITH
NOBLEY, JOANNE
NOGUEIRA, ANTONIO
NOHRA, RAYMOND
NOHRA, GEORGE
NOLAN, PATRICK

NOLAN, MICHAEL
NOLAN, LEE
NOLAN, HARRY
NOLAN, PATRICK
NOLAN, JAMES
NOONE, NEIL
NOORI, BAHMAN
NORKETT, PAUL
NORMAN, PETER
NORRIS, RODNEY
NORRIS, DAVID
NORTHEY, JASON
NORTON, ROBERT
NORTON, ADAM
NORTON, PETER
NOTLEY, ADAM
NOVAK, JAMES JOHN
NOVAKOVIC, MIROSLAV
NOY, BRADLEY CRAIG
NUGENT, DAVID
NUNER, MARK
NUON, SAYONARA
NUPPONEN, MAUNO KALEVI
NUPPONEN, NICK HUGO
NUPPONEN, PETER
O CONNOR, CHRIS
O DONNELL, JAMES
O HAONGHUSA, DIARMAID
O' CONNELL, TREVOR
O'BRIAN, CLEM
O'BRIEN, BRENDAN
O'BRIEN, TREVOR
O'BRIEN, JOHN
O'BRIEN, PASCAL
O'BRYAN, JACK
O'CONNELL, FINBARR
O'CONNELL, IVAN
O'CONNER, BRIAN
O'CONNOR, PATRICK
O'CONNOR, GALEN
O'CONNOR, ADRIAN
O'CONNOR, DONAL
O'DONNELL, LES ROBERT
O'DWYER, MICHAEL
O'HALLORAN, MICHAEL
O'HANLON, WALTER
O'HARA, PATRICK
O'HARA, PATRICK
O'HEARN, AUSTIN
O'KANE, DEAN
O'KEEFE, MICHAEL
O'KEEFE, FRANK
O'KEEFFE, RICHARD
O'LEARY, THOMAS
O'LEARY, DAVID
O'LEARY, BILL
O'LEARY, PAUL
O'LEARY, DENIS
O'LOUGHLIN, SIMON PETER

O'MAHONY, PAUL
O'MALLEY, PATRICK
O'NEAL, RYAN
O'NEIL, JAMES
O'NEIL, BRIAN
O'NEILL, SEAMUS
O'NEILL, MARTIN
O'NEILL, JOHN
O'NEILL, SEAN MICHAEL
O'NEILL, DAVID JOHN
O'NEILL, JOHN
O'NEILL, DANIEL
O'REILLY, GERARD
O'SHANNESSY, MARK
O'SHEA, ANDREW
O'SULLIVAN, TIMOTHY F
O'SULLIVAN, MICHAEL
O'SULLIVAN, MICHAEL
O'NEILL, JOHN
OBIALA, EDMUND
OBIERZYNSKI, GEORGE
OBIERZYNSKI, JOHN
OCALLAGHAN, LUKE
OCH, STEVEN JOHN
ODONNELL, WILLIAM PETER
ODONNELL, ANDREW JOHN
ODONOVAN, TONY
OHAGAN, CHARLIE MICHAEL
OHARA, GEOFFREY ALAN
OLDFIELD, NEIL
OLDRIDGE, JASON
OLIVEIRA, ANDRE
OLIVEIRA, SILVANO
OLIVEIRA, JAIME
OLIVERIO, MICK
OLIVIERI, VINCE
OLKINUORA, PEKKA SAKARI
OLSEN, MICHAEL CARL
OLSEN, JEFFERY
OLYMBIOS, PETER
OMMENSEN, STUART
OPETAIA, BILLY
OPFERKUCH, STEPHEN
OPPEDISANO, JOE
ORESKOVIC, MATO
ORLOVIC, MARYANNE
ORO, CLAUDIO
OROURKE, PETER
OROURKE, JOHN
OSBORNE, SCOTT
OSLOJIC, MILENKO
OSMOND, KEVIN
OSTOJIC, MILOS
OURDAS, PAUL
OUTTRIM, LEONARD
OVERTON, DENNIS
OWEN, ARTHUR
OWEN, EVAN GARETH
OWENS, PAUL

OWERS, MICHAEL WAYNE
PACE, MARIO
PACINELLI, LUIGI
PACINI, DANIEL
PACKETT, MICHAEL
PADOVAN, CRAIG
PADROTH, PAUL LEONARD
PAETZOLD, ALLAN
PAEWHENUA, MORRIS
PAFUMI, DEAN
PAGE, RICKY
PAGE, TONY
PAGE, MICHAEL
PAGE, MARK
PAGLIARO, SAM
PAHIS, JIM
PAIK, BYUNG TAE
PAIKEA, MAT
PAIKEA, DANIEL
PAIKEA, WANA RE
PAK, HYUNG SU
PAKALWISKIS, PETER
PAKAU, IRIEA
PALEOLOGOS, MARKOS
PALU, SULI
PALUMBERI, FRANK
PALUMBO, OSVALDO
PAN, WUN-LUNG
PANAGIS, GEORGE
PANAGOPOULOS, JIM
PANAYI, GEORGE
PANDUROV, PETER
PANG, YAN WING
PANOZIC, ANGELO
PANZARINO, JOE
PAOLO, NAPOLITANO
PAPADIMITRIOU, NICHOLAS
PAPADOPOULOS, ALBERT
PAPADOPOULOS, PETER
PAPALEO, VINCENZO
PAPAPETROS, DIMITRIOS
PAPPAS, JIM
PARANGI, FRANK OIKAU
PARANIHI, WINSTON
PARDEY, BRETT PHILLIP
PARIC, NASER
PARIS, WARREN
PARK, YANG-KIL
PARK, BI HO
PARK, YOUNG-JIN
PARKER, NEU
PARKER, DAVID
PARKINSON, STEVEN
PARKINSON, CONOR
PARKINSON, SCOTT
PARMENTER, VICTOR
PARORE, GAVIN
PARRETT, SHAWN
PARROTTINO, NICOLA

PARROTTINO, JOHN
PARRY, STEPHEN
PARSLOW, KEITH LEONARD
PARSONAGE, MURRAY
PARSONS, RAYMOND
PARTER, JOHN
PARTINGTON, CHRIS
PARTRIDGE, GARRY
PARTRIDGE, EVAN
PASCOE, GAVIN JOHN
PASCUZZO, SANTO
PASK, ROHAN
PASQUA, VITO
PASSFIELD, ADAM LUKE
PATANE, ALLAN
PATCHING, ALAN
PATERSON, JAMES
PATERSON, STEPHEN
PATERSON, GRAEME
PATERSON, NORMAN
PATERSON, DENIS
PATERSON, BLAIR
PATERSON, JAMES GERALD
PATIENT, MARCUS
PATTERSON, ROBERT
PATTERSON, COLIN
PATTERSON, JUSTINE
PATTINSON, LEIGH
PAUL, STEVEN
PAUL, DUNCAN
PAUL, DEREK
PAULL, STEVEN JOHN
PAVEY, DARREL
PAYNE, WILLIAM
PAYNE, RICHARD
PAYSENO, LUKE
PEACOCK, FRANK
PEACOCK, LEN
PEACOCK, DAVID
PEARCE, BEN
PEARCE, JASON
PEARCE, DAVID
PEARCE, WILLIAM
PEARCE, COLIN
PEARCE, DARREN
PEARSE, DAVID A.
PEARSON, DALE
PEARSON, PAUL RALPH
PEARSON, CHRIS
PEARSON, DONALD WILLIAM
PECORINI, TIMOTHY ROBERT
PEDERSEN, KARL
PEDERSEN, COLIN JOHN
PEEBLES, SIDNEY
PEHAR, DENNIS
PEIHOPA, PERCY
PELLEGRINI, OSVALDO
PEMBERTON, MARK
PENEHOE, GEORGE

PENEHOE, SEAN
PENEHOE, LEE JOHANNES
PENFOLD, GREGORY
PENNINGS, MICHAEL
PENNISI, JOSEPH
PENNY, ANDREW
PEPPERALL, COREY
PERCIVAL, KEITH
PERCIVAL, KEVIN
PEREIRA, JOSE
PEREIRA, MANUEL
PEREIRA, FRANCISCO
PEREZ, JOHN
PEREZ, SEBASTIAN
PEREZ, DAVID
PEREZ, ELMER
PEREZ, SEBASTIAN
PERICH, DAREN
PERKINS, PETER
PERKINS, ADAM SHAYNE
PERRI, GIUSEPPE
PERROW, MICHAEL EDWARD
PERRY, MAURICE
PERRY, ROBERT
PERRY, BEN
PETACCIA, PAOLO
PETACCIA, JOE
PETERS, ROBERT
PETERS, DEAN
PETERSEN, ROSS
PETRACK, PETER
PETRIE, GRAHAM
PETRILLO, RENATO
PETROVIC, MIRJAHIA
PETROVSKY, VAS
PETTOVEL, SANTE
PEYROUX, WAYNE
PEZZULIO, JOHN
PFEFFER, TROY EDWARD
PHILIPS, GRAHAM NOEL
PHILLIPS, BRYAN
PHILLIPS, MICHAEL
PHILLIPS, WARREN
PHILLIPS, ANDREW
PHILLIPS, RAE
PHILLIPS, MAXWELL JOHN
PHILLPOT, BEN
PHILPS, REX
PHO, CHONG HYUN
PIATEK, RICHARD
PICCIONI, ALFONSO
PICCLES, JOHN
PICCOLO, MICHAEL
PICKSLEY, JONATHAN
PIDCOCK, JEREMY
CHRISTOPHER
PIETILAINEN, JUMANI
PIKE, KEITH
PILBEAM, DARREN

PILIC, MIRKO
PILISKIC, IVICA
PILLAY, NEIL
PILMER, AARON
PILZ, RICHARD ASTON
PIMM, MICHAEL JOHN
PING-NAM, JOEL
PINKHAM, TAYLOR
PINNIGER, WAYNE
PINNOCK, RICHARD
PINPIN, NOEL
PINTO, ADOLFO SERGIO
PINTO, ANTONIO
PIONA, GERALDO
PIRRI, CARMELO
PISTIKOUDIS, CHRIS
PIZARRO, DAVID FRANCIS
PLAPER, SCOTT
PLAYFORD, CHRIS
PLAYFORD, MICHEAL JAMES
PLENTINGER, MARTIN
PLJAKIC, MEHO
POCRNJA, MIKAN
POLAND, DALE
POLIAS, JOHN
POLITZ, CHRIS
POLIZZI, ANTONIO
POLJAK, ANTE
PONINI, MAARA
POOI, LIONGI
POOLE, SEAN
POOLE, KENNETH BRUCE
POPE, GRAEME
POPE, ALAN JOHN
POPOVIC, MIRKO
PORIO, TEKAO
PORTELA, RICARDO
PORTELLI, RON
PORTER, BARRY
PORTER, JOHN
PORTER, ROBERT
POSA, YURI
POTORU, TEREMAKI
POTTER, LUKE JOHN
POTTER, JAMES
POTTER, ROHAN
POTTS, ALAIN
POULLOS, LEO
POULOS, PETER
POULOS, ANASTASIOS
POWELL, ALAN
POWELL, STEPHEN JOHN
POWELL, LEE DOUGLAS
POWER, KEVIN
POWER, DAVID
POWER, WALTER
POWER, BRIAN FRANCIS
POWTER, ANTHONY DAVID
POZDER, MILORAD

POZZOLUUNGO, ANTONIO
PRACY, DAVID
PRAK, SEUNG SUK
PRASAD, NARENDRA
PRATER, NEIL
PREIST, STEPHEN
PREIST, GLENN
PRELJEVIC, MIRALEM
PRELLER, RUPERT
PRESKETT, GLEN RICHARD
PRESS, PETER
PRESTON, MARKUS
PRESTON, ROD
PREVEDELLO, ANTONIO
PREVETERA, ANDREW
PRIBULA, MICHAEL
PRIBULA, BRETT
PRIBULA, STEPHEN
PRICE, CHRISTOPHER
PRICE, ANTHONY
PRIME, STEPHEN
PRINCE, BOB
PRITCHARD, LUKE
PRITCHARD, DEAN
PRIVITERA, SANTO
PROCHOWSKI, EDMUND
PROCTOR, BENJAMIN
PROCTOR, JUSTIN
PROTHEROE?, BRADLEY JOHN
PROVENZALE, CLAUDIO
PROVENZALE, ROBERT
PROVENZALE, SAM
PROVENZANO, DANIELLE
GRACE
PRPIC, ANTONY PETER
PRPIC, ANTHONY
PRSES, MERSUDIN
PRSKALO, MIJO
PRYCE, MICHAEL
PSARRAS, GEORGE
PUCHER, PETER
PUCKERIDGE, BRENDAN
PUGLIA, TONY
PULGARIN, CASTO
PULIAFICO, TONY
PULJIZ, JOSIP
PUPOVAC, MLADEN
PUPOVAC, KRSTE
PURDIE, RUSSELL
PUREAU, CHRISTOPHER
PURTELL, WAYNE DENIS
QUAGLIA, CARLOS
QUAN, CHANG LU
QUARM, BRETT
QUARTERMAN, ALAN ROGER
QUERIN, STEVEN
QUERIN, GIUSEPPE
QUIGG, JAMES
QUIGLEY, CONOR

QUINN, GRAEME
QUINN, SANDY
QUINN, JEREMY
QUINN, BEN
QUINTAL, BILL
QUINTANA, TEODORO
RABEL, LAURENT
RABER, GENNA
RADANOVIC, ZORAN
RADFORD, JASON CHARLES
RADIC, MATE
RADIS, IVO
RADLOVIC, ZORAN
RAE, DAVID
RAEINA, MANA
RAES, JULES
RAGGETT, BARRY
RAHME, JOHN
RAIC, PREDRAG
RAK, ZELJKO
RAK, JOSIP
RAKIC, SVETO
RALJEVIC, VIKTOR
RALJEVIC, DARIKO
RALPH, DAMIEN
RALPHS, ANDREW
RAMAN, BOB
RAMEA, OLIVIER
RAMIREZ, CARLOS
RAMIREZ, MANUEL
RAMIZ, KAPUR
RAMOVIC, ESED
RAMSAY, ALEX
RAMSAY, DON
RAMSBOTTOM, PETER
RANCE, DENIS
RANCIC, VELJKO
RANDALL, SHANE
RANDAZZO, GIUSEPPE
RANDELL, TODD
RANDELL, ROBERT
RANDELL, ROSEMARY
RANSLEY, NATHAN DOUGLAS
RANTANEN, JOHN
RAPISARDA, ALF
RAPITI, DANIEL
RAPLEY, TALBOT
RATH, PETER
RATKOVIC, DRAGO
RAUDONIKIS, LINCOLN
RAWHITI, SONNY
RAWIRI, DOUG
RAWNSLEY, PATRICK
RAY, THOMAS
RAY, ROSCOE GORDON
RAY, HAROLD
RAY, DAVID
RAY, BILL
RAYMENT, JEFFREY

RAYNER, CHRIS
RAYNER, LINDSAY GEORGE
READ, AARON
READ, ROD
READ, MARK JAMES
READE, STEPHEN
REARDON, DEREK
RECH, RICK
REDDACLIFF, ERIC
REDDY, VINOD
REDFERN, BRIAN TREVOR
REDINGTON, WAYNE
REDOBLADO, JUAN
REDWOOD, BRUNO HAROLD
REDZEPAGIC, FIKRET
REECE, SHANE
REED, CLINTON
REES, GEOFFREY RICHARD
REEVE, BILL
REEVES, BRIAN
REID, BRENT
REILLY, JOHN
REILLY, PAUL JAMES
REIRI, ROBIN HAMI IHAKA
REIRI, ASHLEY
RENNIE, GORDON
RENNIE, ANDREW
RENSHAW, JEFF
REPANELLIS, PAUL
REVELL, STEPHEN RUSSELL
REWAK, BORIS
REWI, NEWTON
REY, ALFRED
REYNOLDS, NICHOLAS CRAIG
REYNOLDS, DENNIS
RIBEIRO, LUIS COSTA
RIBEIRO MACEDO, GUY
MANUEL
RICH, SHANE
RICH, MATTHEW JAMES
RICH, IAN
RICHARDS, PHILLIP
RICHARDS, JASON
RICHARDS, NEIL
RICHARDS, PAUL
RICHARDSON, EDWARD
RICHARDSON, DAVIED
RICHARDSON, KEVIN
SPENCER
RICHARDSON, DEAN
RICHENS, DARREN WILLIAM
(BEN)
RICHMOND, FIONA
RICHMOND, CRAIG
RICKARDS, GRAEME
RICKUS, KONUI
RIDINGS, ROBERT JOHN
RIDLEY, JAMIE
RIGGIO, IGNAZIO

RIGGS, ROBERT
RIGHI, TESSA
RIKALOSKI, SPASE
RIMAC, VATROSLAV
RINGIAO, CLEMENT
RISCO, OSWALD
RITANI, ANTON
RIVERA, JUAN ALEJANDRO
RIVIERA, MICHAEL ANGELO
RIXON, STEPHEN JAMES
RIZKALLA, EMGED
RIZZO, PETER
ROBB, JOHN
ROBERTS, MEREDITH
ROBERTS, DAVID
ROBERTS, STEPHEN
ROBERTS, MICHAEL
ROBERTS, SEAN
ROBERTS, JAMES
ROBERTS, GREG
ROBERTS, WILLIE
ROBERTS, ALBERT
ROBERTS, MICHAEL
ROBERTSON, MARVIN
ROBERTSON, GLEN
ROBERTSON, JOHN
ROBERTSON, GLEN
ROBERTSON, WILLIAM
ROBINETTE, SAMUEL JAMES
ROBINSON, GRAHAM LESLIE
ROBINSON, PETER
ROBINSON, RAY
ROBSON, GORDON JOHN
ROBSON, BRADLEY
ROBSON, RON
ROBSONE?, ROLY?
ROCHA, ANTONIO
ROCHA, VIRGILIO
ROCHE, PAT
RODRIGUES, MARIO
RODRIGUES, JOSE
RODRIGUES, FERNANDO
RODRIGUES, ANTONIO
RODRIGUEZ, LISARDO
RODRIGUEZ, MIGUEL
RODWELL, JACQUELINE ANN
RODWELL, STEPHEN
ROE, MICHAEL
ROELFSEMA, CHRIS
ROGAN, BOB
ROGER, PETER
ROGERS, ANTHONY
ROGERS, PETER
ROGERS, CRAIG
ROGUT, BRIAN
ROIAURI, JAMES
ROIAURI, MARINO
ROIG, RAYMOND
ROIG, DANIEL

ROJAS, PATRICIO	RUSSELL, BRYAN	SANDS, JASON	SCHULTZ, WAYNE	SHEARY, JOHN	SIMSHAUSER, RICHARD	SMITH, MARK ANTHONY	SORIC, ANTE
ROJAS, PAOLA	RUSSELL, ANDREW ALAN	SANDS, DARREN	SCHULZ, RYAN	SHEATHER, BOB	SINCEK, JOHN	SMITH, BRENDAN	SORTWELL, DEREK
ROLLS, ROBERT	RUSSELL, CHRIS	SANG-YONG, KIM	SCHULZ, ANTHONY	SHEEDY, JAMES	SINDONI, DANIEL	SMITH, IAN	SOTIRIOU, STEVE
ROLLS, ERIC	RUSSELL, MICHAEL	SANHUEZA, JULIO	SCHUMACHER, RICK	SHEEDY, PHILLIP	SINDONI, RICHARD	SMITH, ROBERT	SOU, SEREY
ROMANO, RICHARD J	RUSSELL, DAVID	SANKOVIC, BOZO	SCICLUNA, JOHN	SHEEHY, STEVE	SINDONI, UMBERTO	SMITH, JAMES	SOUSA, ANTONIO
ROMANO, MAURICE	RUSSO, NUNZIO	SANTELMANN, STEPHEN	SCIOSCIA, ANTONIO	SHEELEY, LESLIE JOHN	SINDONI, ORAZIO	SMITH, ROBERT	SOUSA, CARLOS
ROMERO, PABLO ERNESTO	RUSSO, JOHN	SANTELMANN, STEPHEN	SCLOSA, UMBERTO	SHEELEY, MICHAEL	SINDONI, CARMELO	SMITH, BRUCE	SOUTHCOMBE, ALLAN
ROMERO, HECTOR NERY	RUSSO, SAM	SANTIC, JOSIP	SCOBIE, JEFF	SHEILDS, KRIS	SINGH, KULDIP	SMITH, DARYL	SOVANNPOV, SAM
RONA, TOM	RUSSO, ANTHONY JOHN	SANTON, DANIEL	SCOGNAMIGLIO, ANTHONY	SHELDON, SCOTT	SINGH, NIRANJAN	SMITH, GORDON	SPAHR, JAOQUES
RONAKI, TAMA	RUSSON, JAMES	SANTOS, JULIO	SCOTLAND, BRUCE	SHEPHERD, ROSS	SINGLETON, ALAN	SMITH, PAUL	SPALDING, CHRIS
ROOKE, PETER JAMES	RUTHERFORD, DENNIS	SANTOS, ANTERO	SCOTT, ROBERT	SHEPHERD, ROBERT	SINNOTT, GORDON	SMITH, GRAEME	SPANNAGL, KIM
ROOKES, DAVID	RYAN, GERARD JOHN	SANTOS, TONY	SCOTT, LINDSAY ROBERT	SHEPHERD, PETER	SIOMIN, ALEXANDER	SMITH, KIM	SPATARO, CON
ROPER, COLIN	RYAN, PATRICK JOHN	SANTOS, PLACIDO	SCOTT, JAMES WILMOT	SHERACK, ROGER	SIPONEN, KEIJO TAPANI	SMITH, BENEJAMIN RAE	SPEARS, DANNY
ROPPOLA, ANTTI	RYAN, KEITH JOHN	SARAFOV, SIMEON	SCOTT, STEPHEN	SHERIDAN, TOM	SIROL, NARCIS	SMITH, JASON BRETT	SPECIALE, FELICE
ROSA, ROBERT	RYAN, AENGUS	SARAIKIN, VASILY	SCOTT, ROBERT	SHERIDAN, JOHN	SIROL, ANTON	SMITH, JUSTIN	SPEECHLEY, RAYMOND
ROSATI, WASYL	RYAN, SHANE	SARD, LACHLAN	SCOTT, BEN	SHERIDAN, ROBERT MAX	SISINNI, ROBBIE	SMITH, WARREN	SPENCER, MARK
ROSE, DARREN	RYAN, JOHN	SARGEANT, STEPHEN	SCOTT, KEVIN	SHERRIFF, JAMES MURRAY	SISK, BRIAN THOMAS MARTIN	SMITH, GARRY	SPENCER, RALPH
ROSE, SCOTT	RYAN, LAWRENCE	SARGENT, PAUL	SCOWCROFT, ROBERT	SHIN, EDWARD	SITARAS, XENOPHON [ZEN]	SMITH, MALCOLM	SPENCER, JOHN
ROSE, PETER	RYAN, BERNARD	SARHAN, ALI	SCUDAMORE, MALCOLM	SHIPARD, DARREN ANDREW	SIVRIC, ILKO	SMITH, NEIL	SPIEGEL, ANDREI
ROSEMOND, JAMES	RYAN, LUKE	SARIC, TADE	SE JIN, LEE	SHIPMAN, DAN	SKARA, DINKO	SMITH, JOHN	SPILLER, HEATH JONATHON
ROSS, ALEC	RYAN, MARK	SARIC, HARRY	SEAGROTT, MARK JOHN	SHORT, PARORO	SKENE, DUNCAN	SMITH, STEVEN	SPILLER, WARICK LUKE
ROSS, ANDREW	RYAN, JASON GREGORY	SARIC, MILAN	SEFO, FIAMALO	SHORT, EDWARD	SKINKYS, ARNOLDAS	SMITH, WARREN	SPINA, MARIO NICHOLAS
ROSS, DANIEL	RYAN, VINCENT	SARIC, HEDJEYKO	SEHIC, MUJO	SHUTTLEWORTH, BERNARD	SKINNER, RICHARD	SMITH, ARTHUR	SPINAZZOLA, GIUSEPPE
ROSS, STEWART	RYMAN, GRANT WALTER	SARKIS, SALAMON	SEHIC, SEMSO	SIDDONS, RICKY	SKINNER, LUKE	SMITH, BRUCE	SPINETTI, CARLO CLAUDIO
ROSS, GORDON	RYPINSKI, JACK	SARRIS, STEVE	SELBY, SHANE MICHAEL	SIDDONS, KIM	SKINNER, MARK	SMITH, ROHAN	SPINETTI, ROBERT
ROSS, KEVIN	SABA, TONY	SARTI, PETER	SELLARS, ANDREW	SIDNEY, JAY HIKI	SKINNER, DAVID	SMITH, ROSS	SPINETTI, PAUL
ROSSI, NICOLA	SABAN, BLAZ	SAULS, SYDNEY	SEMENON, VITALY	SIEDERS, JAN	SKINNER, BRYAN	SMITH, LUKE OSBORN	SPINKS, WILLIAM
ROSSI, NICHOLAS	SABOUNE, MOUSTAPHA	SAUNDERS, STEVEN	SEMENOV, ALEX	SIEDERS, HENARY	SKIPPON, MARC	SMITH, WAYNE	SPINKS, JANICE
ROUMANOS, PAUL	SADER, JOSEPH	SAUNDERS, DAVID	SEMENOV, ALEX	SIHCATO, ORAZIO	SKIRKA, INGRID	SMITH, GREGORY MICHAEL	SPINKS, WAYNE
ROUSSETY, JOHN	SADO, JUAN SAL	SAUNDERS, ROD	SEMINARA, SALVATORE	SILICATO, PHILLIP	SKONDRO, MIRKO	SMITH, RAYMOND JAMES	SPITERI, ALEX
ROUTSIOS, GEORGE	SAEZ, ALEJANDRO	SAUVAO, JOHNSON	SEN, SALY	SILVA, CLAUDIO	SKORIC, ZIVKO	SMITH, DENNIS	SPOONER, DARREN
ROUVRAY, BENJAMIN JOHN	SAFARIK, ANTON	SAVAGE, BARRY ALAN	SENNA, ALDO	SILVA, MANUEL	SKORUP, MILE	SMITH, BENSON	SPRACK, JUSTIN
ROVIRA, FRANCISCO	SAIN, NEVIO	SAVELOS, SAVAS	SEO, BO YOUNG	SILVA, ARLINDO	SKURATOWSKI, ANTON	SMITH, GORDON	SPRADBROW, PETER
ROVIRA, MANUEL	SAIN, NEVIO ROBBIE	SAVIANE, ROBERT	SEO, DONG CHUL	SILVA, JAIME	SLACK, ANTHONY	SMITH, GLENN RONALD	SPRENT, IAN
ROWE, WAYNE	SAIN, ROBBI	SAVIDIS, PETER	SERHAN, SERHAN	SILVA, PATRICIA	SLACK, NATHAN	SMORCHEVSKY, GEORGE	SPROTTE, PETER
ROWE, JEFFERY	SAKKAR, ROBERT	SAVVIDES, GEORGE	SEROTZKI, ADRIAN	SILVA, MARIO	SLAGER, PHILL	SMURTHWAITE, PHILIP	SPROULE, CHRIS
ROWE, ANTHONY RICHARD	SALA, JAMES	SAVVIDES, PETER	SETON, PETER	SILVESTER, KRIS	SLATER, GRAEME	SMYTH, WAYNE	SPROULE, MARTIN
ROWE, GARRY	SALE, ALAN	SAWKA, MYRON	SETON, DAVID	SILVESTRO, ANASTARO	SLATER, NEVILLE	SMYTHE, ANGELA	SPUDVILAS, RON
ROWELL, PETER	SALEH, ABDALLA	SAWYER, REG	SEUNG HO, LEE	SIMIC, IVAN	SLEE, RICHARD	SNOCH, MARGARET	SQUADRITO, JOE
ROWINSKI, RICHARD	SALIB, MICHAEL	SAYED, AZZAM	SEWELL, PAUL DAVID	SIMIC, MICHAEL	SLIBRITZKY, ROBERT	SNODGRASS, ANDREW	SQUADRITO, CARMELO
ROWLANDS, DAMIEN	SALIBA, RICHARD	SAYERS, NIGEL	SEYMOUR, ROSS WILLIAM	SIMIONE, MICHAEL	SLOAN, ROSS	SNOWDON, PETER	SRECKOVIC, MILAN
ROWLANDS, CHRIS	SALIMI, VEAP	SCALES, ANDREW	SHAH, AFZAL	SIMMONS, JOHN	SLOANE, RODNEY	SO, WAI MAN	SRECKOVIC, JASMINKA
ROZAKIS, JIM ANTHONY	SALMON, BEN	SCALTRITO, JOE	SHAHMATOV, GREG	SIMMONS, PATRICK	SLOEY, JASON	SOARES, ELSON FERREIRA	SRSA, MIODRAG
ROZIC, FLAMENGO	SALTER, STEVEN	SCALZO, ALDO	SHAKHTOUR, OMAR	SIMMONS, KIRK	SLOGGETT, DEAN	SOELLNER, NEAL	ST JOHN, NICHOLAS
RUAWAI, MICHAEL	SALVARTSIS, THEODOSIOS	SCARCELLA, ANGELO	SHANAHAN, DANIEL JOSEPH	SIMMONS, PAUL	SLOT, TONY	SOHAIL, WASIM	STACEY, NATHAN
RUBBO, MARIO	SAMMUT, CHARLES	SCARD, JOHN	SHANDON, MARK	SIMMUL, ULO	SLY, PAUL	SOKOL, IVAN	STACH, RICHARD
RUDDICK, BRETT	SAMONI, MARCO	SCARFE, STEPHEN JOHN	SHANKS, ROSS	SIMOES, JORGE	SLYM, MICHAEL	SOLARI, TONY	STACK, STEPHEN
RUFATT, PATRICK	SAMORUKOFF, VAS	SCARR, GREGORY BRENT	SHANNON, CHARLES	SIMOES, JOSE	SMALL, GRAEME	SOLARI, MARCOS	STAFFORD, MARK
RUGGIERO, MAURO	SAMPAIO, CARLOS	SCEENEN, MARK	SHARMAN, GORDON	SIMON, DOUGLAS	SMALL, PETER	SOLBIATI, STEFANO	STAINER, BENJAMIN
RUHL, MATT	SAMPERI, ROSS	SCHAUMKEL, ALEKI	SHARP, ROBERT JOHN	SIMON, GREG	SMALL, WILLIAM	SOLEM, JAN	STAINES, GREGORY PETER
RUISI, MARCELLO	SAMPSON, PAUL	SCHAUMKEL, KENNETH	SHARP, ANDREW	SIMON, SCOTT	SMALL, IAN	SOLLY, PETER JAMES	STAINES, PAUL ROBERT
RUIZ, CLAUDIO	SANCHEZ, MIGUEL	SCHEUL, PHILIP	SHARPHAM, LEIF	SIMONATO, GARY	SMART, MATTHEW	SOLTAU, STUART	STAIRMAND, DEREK
RUJAK, VELIBOR	SANCHEZ, WALTER	SCHINDLER, MAURICE	SHARPHAM, BOB	SIMONORSIG, ZIVKO	SMITH, STEPHEN JOHN	SOLWAY, MATTHEW	STALEY, WAYNE
RULE, GARY	SANCHEZ, JUAN CARLOS	SCHMIDT, PETER	SHAW, DAMIEN	SIMPSON, LLOYD WILLIAM	SMITH, DANIEL	SOMMERVILLE, ALLAN	STANCZYK, JOSHUA
RUMBLE, BILL	SANCHEZ, DARIO	SCHMIDT, ALEXANDER	SHAW, LUKE	SIMPSON, DAVID	SMITH, KELSEY	SOO YUNG, HA	STANGER, JEFFREY
RUMPH, SCOTT	SANCHEZ, IRVING	SCHNEIDER, RAYMOND	SHEA, TIM	SIMPSON, GARTH	SMITH, JOHN ARTHUR	SOON MAN, KWON	STANLEY, PHILIP
RUPCIC, STEVE	SANDER, GUSTAVO	SCHOEMAKER, ANDREW	SHEA, GREGORY	SIMPSON, PIERRE SIMON	SMITH, MICHAEL ALAN	SOPHODEOUS, MICHAEL	STANLEY, DAVID
RUPCIC, PATRICK	SANDERS, GLENN	SCHOOLING, JOHN	SHEARER, ANDREW	SIMPSON, JOHN	SMITH, ANDREW OSBORN	SORBELLO, GIUSEPPE	STANTE, ADAM
RUPCIC, JOE	SANDERSON, GLEN	SCHRIEVER, IVO	SHEARER, JOHN	SIMPSON, ROBERT	SMITH, CRAIG LIONEL	SORIA, JUAN	STARK, JOSEPH

STARKS, STEPHEN
STARR, JOHN
STAVREVSKI, ALEKSANDAR
STEAD, DEAN DAVID
STEADMAN, JOHN
STEDFORD, RON
STEDMAN, GLEN
STEEL, ANTHONY
STEER, JOHN
STEGNJAIC, MILORAD
STEIMBEISSER, ADOLFO
STELLINO, WAYNE
STEPHENS, JUSTEN
STEPHENS, ABRAHAM
STEPHENSON, ANDREW
STEPTOE, MICHAEL
STERGIOTIS, DAVID ANGELO
STERLING, PHIL
STEVAN, CUPAC
STEVENS, MITCH
STEVENS, RONALD
STEVENS, THOMAS
STEVENS, KENNETH JAMES
STEVENSON, GREG ROBERT
STEVILL, STAN
STEWART, CHRISTINE ANNE
STEWART, DAVID
STEWART, GEORGE
STEWART, MARK
STEWART, ROBERT
STEWART, GRAEME
STEWART, NICHOLAS
STEWART, SIMON
STEWART, DARREN
STEWART, WADE ANDREW
STEWART, SHANE
STEWART, PETER
STIH, DRAGO
STIKOVIC, ROBERT JOSEPH
STOFREGEN, STEVEN
STOJANOSKI, DUKO
STOJKOVSKI, LUPCO
STOJSIC, DENIS
STOJSIC, JOHN
STOJSIC, ZARKO
STONOGA, WAGNER
STORATH, ROBERT
STORER, GRAHAM
STORMON, ALLEN
STOUPIS, NICK
STRADA, JOHN
STRANG, PAUL
STRASSHAFER, STEVEN
STRAUSS, ROD
STRBAC, MIO
STRBAC, MARKO
STRETCH, JONATHAN
STROCCHI, JACK
STRONG, MICHAEL

STRONG, NICK
STROUD, PAUL
STUART, CRAIG
STUART, JASON
STUART, BENJAMIN
STUBBS, GREG
STUDMAN, TREVOR JOHN
STUGEON, JOHN
STURBEN, COLIN
STURGEON, REECE
STUTCHBURY, DAVID
STUTTLE, WILLIAM
STYLIANOU, PAUL
SUAREZ, ALEXANDRO
SUAREZ, PAUL
SUAREZ, RUBEN CLEMENTS
SUBRITZKY, HARRY
SUBRITZKY, DARRYL
SUGAR, JOHN PETER
SUGDEN, MATTHEW
SUGGATE, KEVIN
SUH, JONG SOO
SUKKAR, CHARLIE
SUKNOVIC, PETER
SULLIVAN, LIAM
SULLIVAN, ADAM
SULLY, JASON
SUMI, PAUL
SUN, ROBERT
SUN, CHUN ZE
SUN, HONG SOON
SUN, CHUN ZHE
SUSAK, DRAGAN
SUSANJ, IVAN
SUSNJARA, IVANKA
SUTCLIFFE, JACK
SUTERS, ANTHONY
SUTHERLAND, ROBERT
SUTHERLAND, ALLAN
SUTHERLAND, ANDREW
SUTHERLAND, CHRIS
SUTINEN, GARY ALLAN
SUTTON, NATHAN
SVENSSON, JOHAN
SVORINIC, JULIO
SWAIN, PAUL
SWAIN, PETER JOHN
SWAINE, KEITH
SWART, TIM
SWEENEY, PETER
SWEENEY, JONATHAN
SWEET, TODD
SYDENHAM, BRUCE
SYMMONDS, JON LEE HENRY
SYMONS, WAYNE TREVOR
SYRCH, WAYNE
SYRON, GARY
SZECKO, EDWARD
SZECKO, VICTOR

SZWAJA, KRZYSZTOF
TABEIRA, GERVASIO
TABONE, HUGH
TACIC, MOMIR
TADDIO, TONY
TADIC, BOZO
TADIC, JOZO
TAHAN, KHALED
TAI XIAN, JIN
TAIAROA, VICTOR
TAKAHASHI, AYUMU
TAKI, RYAN
TALEVSKI, TONY
TAMAGNO, PETER
TAMBOURAS, PETER MICHAEL
TAMPOLJA, MOMCILO
TAMSETT, EDWARD JOHN
TANG, ANTHONY
TANGYE, DARREN
TANNOCK, GREG
TAPIA, CLAUDIA
TARANTO, DOMINIC
TARGARONA, FRANK
TARRANT, LEIGH
TARTAGLIA, JERRY
TARTTANEN, TIMO
TASSIOS, GEORGE
TASUKI, SETO
TATHAM, STEVEN
TATUM, PHILIP
TATUM, DANE
TAUHINU, ARTHUR
TAURA, VAINETUTAI
TAVARES, LUDGERO DE OLIVEIRA
TAWAKE, JOSH
TAYLOR, GRANT
TAYLOR, GREG
TAYLOR, CHRIS
TAYLOR, MARK
TAYLOR, BRIAN
TAYLOR, GREG
TAYLOR, GARY
TAYLOR, MATTHEW
TAYLOR, LISETTE
TAYLOR, NEIL
TAYLOR, BARRY
TAYLOR, PAUL
TAYLOR, STEPHEN
TAYLOR, PETER
TAYLOR, STEPHEN
TAYLOR, MARK
TAYLOR, EDWARD (PEPE)
TCHEPAK, SLAV
TE AWHITU, DAVID
TEAO, UPOKOMAKI
TEDESCO, ANGUS
TELFORD, SEAN
TEMPLAR, JAMES

TEMPLETON, KEITH
TEMPLEWATTS, TREVOR
TENETI, VICTOR
TEOFILOVIC, GEORGE
TEPSA, BORIS
TERAKI, JASON
TERS, MICHAEL
TETEVANO, TAMAINE CHRISTIAN
TEUA, JOHN
TEUMA, MATTHEW
THACKRAY, STUART
THEAKSTON, IVAN
THEMESTOKLYS, PETER
THEODORAKOPOULOS, KOSTA
THEODORAKOPOULOS, LEONIDAS
THEODOROU, THEO
THEW, MICHAEL
THEYERS, CHRISTOPHER
THIEDEKE, DARRYL
THIRLWELL, PETER
THOMAS, ANGELA CATHERINE
THOMAS, COLIN EDMUND
THOMAS, ANAND
THOMPSON, JOHN
THOMPSON, MICHAEL
THOMPSON, JASON
THOMPSON, GLEN
THOMPSON, JOHN
THOMPSON, ROCKY
THOMPSON, DENNIS
THOMPSON, IAN MARTIN
THOMPSON, SHANE
THOMPSON, BARRY
THOMPSON, GLEN
THOMPSON, HAROLD
THOMSON, KEN
THOMSON, JEFFREY
THOMSON, LLOYD
THOMSON, NEVILLE JAMES
THORN, MARTIN
THORNE, PETER
THORNE, JASON
THORNTON, JACK
THURGOOD, JOHN
THURTELL, GREGORY JOHN
TIATIA, HENRY
TIERNEY, JAMES
TIERNEY, MICHAEL
TIERNEY, BRETT
TIGHE, JAMIE AUSTIN
TIHEMA, TAI
TILIAKOS, STAVROS
TILL, ROD
TILLER, DALLAS
TILLHON, JOHN

TILLING, ROBERT
TILOCCA, SALVATORE
TIMOTI, TED
TINA, ANGIE
TINA, GRANT
TINKER, PATRICK
TINKER, MICHAEL
TIRANT, BRETT
TITMARSH, JOHN
TITONE, ARMANDO
TITONE, GIUSEPPE
TITONE, CARLO
TITONE, NICOLA
TODD, DAVID
TODD, ADAM
TODD, KEITH
TODOROVIC, MICK
TOFFOLON, MARK
TOHME, ALEXI
TOIA, JOHN CHRISTOPHER
TOIA, HAROLD CHARLES
TOKONA, STEVEN
TOLHURST, PETER
TOLOMEO, JOSEPH GERARD
TOM, ADAM
TOMANOVIC, ROBERT
TOMARCHIO, RICK
TOMAS, JERRY
TOMASETTI, CRAIG
TOMMASO, TONY
TOMS, PAUL CLAYTON
TONG, EDWARD
TOOLE, IVAN
TOPIC, NEDELJKO
TOPPING, ANTONIO
TORO, RUTH
TORRESAN, IVO PAOLO
TORRISI, JOHN
TOWNSEND, ALLAN
TOWNSEND, ADAM
TRACEY, JOHN
TRACY, MICHAEL
TRAD, ROBERT JAMES
TRAINOR, CHRIS
TRAINOR, DONAL
TRAM, PHILLIP
TRAN, TERRENCE
TRAN, HAU
TRAN, TUAN MINH
TRAN, RIEN
TRANTER, PETER
TRAPOLINI, MIGUEL
TRAPPETT, TOD
TRAVERS, DEAN
TRAVIS, CLINTON
TRELOYN, CAMERON JOHN

TREMAIN, BARRIE RAYMOND
TRETHOWAN, ADAM
TREVENA, JON MATTHEW
TREWEEK, DAVID
TRIANT, NICK
TRICKETT, CLIVE
TRIEU, PHUNG
TRIPODI, GIOVANNI
TROTTER, ALAN
TROTTER, JAY
TROUTMAN, MICHAEL JOHN
TROVATO, SILVIO
TROY, JOHN
TRPKOSKI, TONY
TRUSTUM, BRIAN
TSAGARAKIS, JIM
TSAKIRIDIS, ANTHONY
TSAPICOUNIS, THEO
TSE, CHEONG
TSOLAKIS, BILL
TSOUTSAS, PETER
TSOVOLOS, ARTHUR
TUATARA, ALF
TUATARA, DONALD
TUCK, STEPHEN
TUGWELL, PETER
TUKARA, IVICA
TUOVINEN, MATTI
TUOVINEN, REIJO
TURNER, GEORGE WILLIAM
TURNER, GREG
TURNER, ERIC
TURNER, CHRIS
TURNER, JEFFREY
TURNER, STEPHEN
TURNER, COLIN MICHAEL
TURPEINEN, TAUNO
TURSKI, PETER ALBIN
TURUNEN, ARTHUR JOSEF
TURVILLE, RICKY
TUTIN, ANTHONY
TWEEDIE, LYNTON
TWEEDIE, BRETT
TWEEDIE, WAYNE
TWISS, JAMES GEORGE
TWOMEY, BEN
TWYMAN, ANDREW
TYLER, PETER JOHN
TYNE, JAMES
UBSDELL, MILES
UH, SHUK HUN
UNDERWOOD, RODD
UNG, LAC HOUN
UPTON, PHILLIP
UPTON, MICHAEL
UREN, NICOLE LOUISE
URIRAU, NGATA
USALJ, JOE
USHER, CRAIG

UYEDA, VICTOR
UZELAC, SASHA
UZELAC, TRIVUN
UZELAC, DJURO GEORGE
UZELAC, DENIS
UZUNOVIC, MIRSADA
VACCARELLA, JOE
VACCARO, ROBERT
VAINGALO, HIKIPOOU
VAISTO, RAIMO
VALARAKOS, TOM
VALDES, OSCAR
VALENTI, ROSS
VALENTI, DOMENICO
VALENTI, MATHEW
VALENZUELA, HUGO
VALESINI, PAUL
VALLETTA, ANTHONY
VALURI, RAJ
VALUS, JOSEF
VAN DE PUTTE, FRANK IVAN
VAN DER HOUWEN, STEPHAN
VAN DORRESTEYN, DESMOND
VAN GELDEREN, ALEX
VAN HAMOND, ANDREW THOMAS
VAN LIEROP, RENE
VAN SON, WONG
VAN YE, NGUYEN
VAN ZANTEN, MARK
VAN ZELM, HANS
VAN ZELM, ALECIA
VAN ZELM, ADRIAN
VANDERMEER, THEODORE
VANDERSEE, STEPHEN BRIAN
VANDERVELDE, BRIAN
VANGESTEL, PIMJOHN
VANZANELLA, TONY
VARRICA, MARCEL
VAS, MICHAEL JOHN
VASARA, MARKKU
VASCO, LUIS
VASILIADIS, GEORGE
VASILIADIS, TONY
VASSALLO, JOHN
VAUGHAN, GARY
VAUGHAN, GARTH
VEECH, DAVID
VEG, ZVONKO
VEGAN, ANDREW
VEIRA, MANUEL
VELASCO GOMEZ, AICARDO
VELEVSKI, ALEKSANDAR
VELJOVIC, PREDRAG
VELLA, ROBERT
VELLA, GEORGE
VELLA, STEPHEN
VELLA, PETER
VELLA, EDWARD JOSEPH

VELLIS, JOHN
VELNIC, ZLATOMIR
VELOZO, MICHAEL
VENOHARAN, SINKAINATHAN
VERMEER, ADRIAN GERARD
VERON, CLAUDIO RICARDO
VERSCHELDEN, SHANE
VERSI, SAJJAD
VIACHESLAV, VOLKOV
VICKERY, BEN
VICTORIA, MANUEL
VIDAL, LUCIANO
VIDIC, ALEKSANDAR
VIDINOPOULOS, VIC
VIEGAS, ANTONIO
VIEGAS, ANTORRIO
VIEIRA, ANTONIO
VIEIRA, MANUEL
VIEIRA, NESTOR
VIEIRA, DALMAR BATISTA
VIEIRA, ORLANDO
VIEIRA, JOSE MANUEL
VILAS BOAS, MANUEL
VINCENT, STEVE
VINE, WARREN
VINHAS, DANIEL
VIRCO, RON
VITAS, MOMIR
VITAS, BOSKO
VITAZ, ALAN
VLAKIC, MARKO
VOGTMANN, KLAUS DIETER
VOTANO, CLAYTON JAMES
VOURLOS, ANGELO
VRACAR, RANKO
VRANKOVIC, JOVAN
VRATARIC, JOE
VRATARIC, JOSO
VU, DONG VAN
VUCIC, MIRKO
VUCKOVIC, DJURO
VUJOVIC, RAJKO (RAY)
VUKALOVIC, STEVE
VUKELIC, MICHAEL
VUKOJA, MIROSLAV
VULCIK, MARIQ
VULETIC, BARISA
VULIC, MARKO
VULIC, SIME
WAAKA, DARYL
WADA, KUNIHIRO
WAGSTAFF, PAUL
WAIHI, CLARENCE
WAINWRIGHT, PAUL
WAITE, THOMAS DION
WAITE, DION
WAKELING, JAMES
WAKELING, MICHAEL
WALDRON, KEVIN

WALKER, PAUL
WALKER, JOHN
WALKER, WESLEY
WALKER, GEORGE
WALKER, CLINT
WALKER, MICK
WALKER, PATRICK
WALKER, JIM
WALKER, PHILIP HARVEY
WALKER, CRAIG
WALKER, PATRICK LEON
WALLACE, IAN
WALLACE, PETER
WALLACE, RAUKAWA
WALLACE, RAYMOND
WALLACE, JOSHUA
WALLACE, DAVID ANDREW
WALLACE, DARREN
WALLACE, GLENN
WALLER, CAMPBELL
WALLIS, DAVID
WALSH, RODNEY
WALSH, ROSS
WALSH, PATRICK JAMES
WALSH, LIAM
WALSH, DENNIS
WALSH, STEVEN
WALTING, LEON
WANA, GEORGE
WANG, JAMES
WANING, KEVIN
WANNA, STEVE
WARBURTON, JOHN
WARD, THOMAS
WARD, MATTHEW
WARD, GARY
WARD, BERNIE
WARD, DAVID
WARD, CHRISTOPHER
WARD, ANDREW
WARD, JASON
WARN, COLIN DESMOND
WARN, MATTHEW
WARNER, MICHAEL JOHN
WARREN, BLAIR
WARREN, SCOTT
WASSALL, ROGER KENNETH
WASSON, DANNY
WATERS, STEPHEN GEORGE
WATKINS, LINDSAY ALLAN
WATKINS, STEVEN
WATLING, CRAIG
WATSON, ERIC
WATSON, PAUL
WATSON, NOEL EDWARD
WATSON, DARREN
WATSON, NEAL
WATSON, DANIEL
WATSON, CHRISTOPHER

WATSON, JAMES
WATTS, GAVIN
WATTS, ANTHONY
WATTS, PETER
WAXHAM, BRIAN
WAY, MARCEL PETER
WEATHERBURN, DENNIS
WEBB, DARRYL EDWARD
WEBB, CHRISTOPHER
WEBB, JOHN
WEBB, ADRIAN
WEBBER, PETER
WEBSTER, NORMAN RONALD
WEBSTER, WILLIAM
WEBSTER, ANDREW
WEEN, DAMON
WEGENER, IAN
WEIR, THOMAS
WEISS, INGO
WELCH, ANDREW
WELLS, WARREN
WELLS, DAMIAN
WELLS, MATHEW
WELLS, TIMOTHY
WELSH, ALLAN
WENZEL, DAVID
WERNER, BO
WESSELING, JOHN
WEST, WARREN CHARLES
WEST, RONALD JAMES
WEST, RICHARD
WEST, BRAD
WEST, ROBERT
WESTALL, MARK
WESTALL, HEATH
WHARE, DEREK
WHAREPOURI, RICK
WHATMORE, JOHN
WHEELER, BRETT
WHEELER, ADRIAN
WHELAN, THOMAS
WHIELDON, BILLY
WHIPPLE, ROBERT JOHN
WHITE, PETER
WHITE, JOHN
WHITE, SHANE
WHITE, JONATHAN LINDSAY
WHITE, DAVID
WHITE, BRETT
WHITE, JOHN
WHITE, AARON PHILLIP
WHITE, ANTHONY
WHITE, NICHOLAS
WHITE, BEN
WHITE, BILL
WHITEHEAD, DICK
WHITEHEAD, ANDREW
WHITEHILL, BRUCE WAYNE
WHITFIELD, ROBERT

WHITIKIA, SIMON
WHITING, BILLY
WHITTON, PETER
WHITTON, GREGORY
WHYBROW, DAVID
WHYMAN, JASON
WHYMAN, NEIL
WHYTE, TERRY
WHYTE, DAVID GERALD
WIECZOREK, DAVID
WIEHRL, JORGE
WIENCKE, MATTHEW PAUL
WIGHTLEY, REX ALLAN
WIJNEN, ANDREW
WILDER, RUSSELL
WILGERMEIN, RAY
WILKENS, SEAN ANTHONY
WILKIE, GORDON
WILKINS, KEITH VICTOR
WILKINS, MICHAEL
WILKINSON, ROBBIE MITCHELL
WILKINSON, ROWLAND
WILKINSON, MICHAEL
WILKINSON, GEOFFREY
WILKS, STEPHEN
WILLIAMS, MICHAEL
WILLIAMS, VICTORIA
WILLIAMS, THOMAS
WILLIAMS, NATHAN SCOTT
WILLIAMS, PAUL
WILLIAMS, RICHARD
WILLIAMS, ANDREW
WILLIAMS, TROY
WILLIAMS, MARK
WILLIAMS, NATHAN
WILLIAMS, MALCOLM
WILLIAMS, NORMAN
WILLIAMS, KELVIN
WILLIAMS, JEFF
WILLIAMSON, RODNEY
WILLIAMSON, MATTHEW
WILLIAMSON, GAVIN
WILLIS, KEITH
WILLIS, MICHAEL
WILLIS, LES
WILLIS, NEVILLE
WILLIS, GARY
WILLMOTT, PETER JOHN
WILLS, KEVIN
WILLS, SIMON
WILLSON, MARK
WILMOT, STEPHEN
WILSHER, ASHLEY
WILSON, TUPARA
WILSON, BRAD
WILSON, GRAEME LESLEY
WILSON, JAMES
WILSON, WARREN

WILSON, SCOTT
WILSON, WILFRED
WILSON, STUART CHARLES
WILSON, RICKY WILLIAM
WILSON, MERUYN
WILSON, JOHN DOUGLAS
WILSON, MARK
WILSON, KENNETH ANDREW
WILSON, MICHAEL
WILSON, GORDON
WILSON, COLIN
WILSON, JASON
WILSON, STEPHEN
WILSON, JEFFREY
WILSON, JAMES
WILSON, WAYNE
WILSON, CARL
WILSON, BARRY
WILSON, PATRICK
WILTON, JAMES
WINDON, PATRICK
WINDUS, JOHN
WINIKEREI, DOUGLAS P
WINKLER, KARL
WINKS, JONATHAN
WINNEY, LLOYD
WINSTANLEY, SCOTT
WINTER, KEVIN
WISE, DARREN
WISEMAN, LEONARD
WISEMEN, MICK
WITANA, SHAYNE
WITCZAK, JAN
WITHERS, PAUL JOHN
WITHERS, TOBY
WITHERS, ADAM
WODECKI, PAUL
WOLF, RUDOLF
WOLSKE, SIEGFRIED
WOLTHERS, BOWMAN MANSON
WON CHUL, LIM
WONG, LIEN FENG
WONG, PATRICK
WONG, MARK
WOOD, WILLIAM
WOOD, ALISON
WOOD, SAM
WOOD, MAX
WOOD, JEREMY
WOOD, GRAEME
WOODFORD, COLIN
WOODHOUSE, STEPHEN
WOODS, GARRY
WOODS, SHANE
WOODS, KEVIN
WOODS, WILLIAM HENRY
WOOLGAR, CRAIG
WOOLLEY, GEOFF ROBERT

WOOLSEY, KEVEN
WOOSTER, SIMON
WOOTTON, STEVEN MARK
WOROBIEJ, WALTER
WORT, RODNEY
WORTHINGTON, ROY
WRIGHT, COLIN
WRIGHT, JOHN
WRIGHT, STEPHEN
WRIGHT, JASON
WRIGHT, GREGORY
WRIGHT, MATTHEW JOHN
WRIGHT, JARROD
WUTZKE, MARIELLA
WYATT, PHILLIP
WYBRON, KEVIN BRUCE
WYBURD, MICHAEL ROBERT
WYLES, NEIL
WYLES, PHIL
XAVIER, NILSON ALVES
XIAO, WENZHONG
XU, ZHENG
YACOUB, ATE
YAHFOUFI, ALI
YALI, DIEGO
YAMMINE, GEORGE
YAN, PING LEI
YAP, JIMMY
YATES, DAVID
YAZBEK, MAL
YEE, GRAHAM
YEN, PIRON
YERMAN, MARINO
YIP, JAMES
YONG, CHEN
YOO, YOUNG-SOO
YOO TACK, WON
YOUNAN, FURID
YOUNAN, JOHN
YOUNAN, TONY
YOUNAN, EDDY
YOUNAN, CHARLIE
YOUNAN, ANTHONY
YOUNG, JAMES B
YOUNG, JOHN
YOUNG, KEVIN
YOUNG, TODD
YOUNG, ROGER
YOUNG, TIM
YOUNG, WILLIE
YOUNG, BRIAN
YOUNG, BARRY
YOUNG, FRED
YOUNG, TRACY
YOUNG, RAYMOND
YOUNG, MATTHEW
YOUNGER, JEFF
YOUSIF, JANSAN
YU, TAE ON

ZABOYAK, MYRON JOESPH
ZADOYAN, NISHAN MURAD
ZAGAMI, BILL
ZAHARIA, NICULAIE
ZALEWSKI, KARL
ZALGHOUT, ABBAS
ZALLOUA, JOSEPH
ZAMMIT, STEVE
ZAMMIT, MICHAEL JOHN
ZAMMIT, TONY
ZANET, GIANNI
ZARKOVIC, VELKO
ZARTH, PETER
ZAURRINI, ALDO
ZDON, CZESKAW
ZEBALLOS, RUBEN RICARDO
ZEBALLOS, ANTONIO
ZELJKOVIC, MILE
ZENKE, PETER
ZHANG, QIANG
ZHENG, CHENG PING
ZHOU, GUI GHUN
ZIELONKO, STEFAN
ZILIC, ILIJA
ZINGALAOA, MEL
ZIVKO, TEPSA
ZIZIC, NIKOLA
ZMUDA, STEVEN
ZOPPELLARO, GIOVANNI
ZREIKA, BASSAM
ZUANIC, ROD
ZUANIC, BRUNO
ZUCCHETTO, CARLO
ZUCCONI, PAUL
ZUNIGA, EDMUNDO
ZUPAN, MILE

The Stadium during one of several large audience events soon after opening. This event was the Centenary Test between Australia and England. The crowd was in excess of 80 000. At the time of going to print, the largest audience housed was for the Bledisloe Cup between Australia's Wallabies and the New Zealand All Blacks—nearly 108 000 people. Maximum capacity is 110 000.